*This book is dedicated to my family
Jen, Corey, Jessie and Josh*

*This book is being sold to the students of
My Body/My Health at cost. The author does not
receive any profit from the sale of the book.*

*The author would also like to acknowledge and thank
Dr. Jane Vella and Dr. Peter Senge for much of the
teachings in this book comes from their work.*

Phred and Me

Daniel Gerber

An Off the Common Book, Amherst, Massachusetts

Printed in the United States of America

ISBN 978-1-937146-87-0

Contents

Chapter One

I always knew I was different than others, but it wasn't until I was fourteen that I first began to understand how and why. It was then that I met Phred. Phred was, and is, a great teacher of life, and Phred wasn't the ordinary kind of friend either. Phred was different, Phred was a parrot. But hang on, I'm getting ahead of myself. I should first introduce myself. After all, I am the author, and while I won't argue that Phred is smarter than me – heck, Phred's smarter than everyone – I am the main character! My name is John. And I'm not fourteen anymore. I'm now twenty-five, but since this is the story of Phred and me, I figure people should envision me as the happy-go-lucky fourteen-year-old boy I was when Phred and I first met.

So, as I have already said, my name is John, and at fourteen I lived in the Florida Keys. My parents managed a small hotel with a dock, and a tiki bar at the end of the dock. Phred liked to hang out at the tiki bar while he waited for me to finish my chores. Living in the Keys, especially where I lived, was a great place to grow up. Oh, the Keys do have a boring suburbia, mostly in the form of tacky trailer parks or cheap cinder block cottages, but I was lucky enough not to live in one of these suburban neighborhoods. I lived next to the hotel alongside a creek. It wasn't much from a financial standpoint, but for me it was perfect. Our house was an old wooden cottage with four rooms: a living room, kitchen, a bedroom for my parents, and a bedroom for me. Off the living room was a porch that bordered a creek. Trees, bushes, and vines surrounded the porch and it was my job to keep the bushes near the creek at a reasonable level. With the bushes cut low my parents and I could sit on the porch, while watching the fish and frogs in the creek, and feel a breeze. Early evening was the best time to sit on the porch because this was the coolest time of day and before the bugs came out. It was on one of these beautiful, cool evenings that I met Phred.

Now, remember Phred's a parrot, and we don't see many parrots in the Keys. The ones we do see usually found their way up from Central America. Anyway, I was sitting on the porch alone early one evening, reading *The Adventures of Tom Sawyer*, when a voice said,

"What are you reading, child?"

"Huh, who said that?" I looked around but didn't see anyone. "Mom, Dad, are either of you guys home?" No one answered.

"YO, child, so what are you reading?" asked the voice.

I looked up and there on one of the low branches sat a parrot. Actually, it was a cockatoo, but to me a cockatoo is just a parrot. "Did you say something, Mr. Parrot?" I asked.

"Cockatoo, son, and yes I did, I asked what are you reading?" said the parrot (I mean cockatoo).

Now, I wasn't sure how to react to a talking parrot, especially one that seemed intelligent. So, for lack of any other idea of what to do, I tried replying and said, "Tom Sawyer."

"Was he a skinny kid who liked to run around with a friend named, ah, Finn?" asked the parrot.

"Huckleberry Finn is his friend's name, and, yes, that's the book," I said.

"The author was a cranky old fool. My great-great-great grandfather used to help him write when he lived up in Hartford, Connecticut. But this was when the author was getting old and all he really wanted to do was play billiards, smoke cigars, drink whiskey, and complain how stupid others were. Good book though," said the parrot.

"Who are you?" I asked, a little annoyed he was putting one of my favorite authors down.

"Oh, excuse my manners, I thought I introduced myself," apologized the parrot. "My name is Phred."

"My name is John," I said. "Am I really talking to a parrot?"

"Cockatoo, son, but if you want to call me a parrot, I guess it's okay. And you're talking to me, and since I am a parrot by your definition, then, yes, you're talking to a parrot. Haven't you ever seen a parrot talk before?" he asked.

"Well, yeah, but never about Tom Sawyer or Mark Twain – I mean Samuel Clemens."

"Have you ever asked a parrot about Mr. Clemens or Tom Sawyer?"

"No," I answered hesitantly, "but that's not what I mean. I mean I never knew parrots were so smart. I thought they just repeated what people say."

"Are you sure you're not thinking about people? Most people I meet are just repeating what other people say," he said. There was a moment of silence before Phred continued, "To clear up some of your confusion, it's true most parrots do just repeat what other people say, but there are a few of us who get tired of that and start to think for ourselves. I suppose there are people like that too."

"Of course there are people like that!" I yelled, but even as I was yelling I knew he had a point. You see, at this point in my life I didn't have many friends. For some reason I just didn't fit in with the other children my age at school. They were always talking about sports and girls, and it wasn't that I didn't like sports and girls, I just can't talk about them all day. During my free time I would stick my nose in a book, and after school I'd head for home, to do chores, go fishing, or explore the creeks and waterways near home.

"Sorry," said Phred, a little put off, "I didn't mean to make you angry. If you want, I'll leave."

"No. No, no, please don't leave. I didn't mean to sound angry. It's just that life is frustrating sometimes," I said.

"Yeah, I know what you mean," Phred said softly. "The reason I stopped in the first place was because you looked lonely."

Before I could respond, the front door of the house opened and my Mom walked in.

"John, I'm home. Where are you?" she called.

"Out here, Mom," I answered. "There is someone I want you to meet."

"John, no, no..." Phred stammered.

"Oh you brought a friend home with you," said Mom as she walked out onto the porch.

"No, Mom, I want you to meet Phred," I said. "He's a parrot, or ah... Cockatoo."

Mom looked around confused at first and then up into the trees. When she finally saw Phred she smiled. "Oh, hello Phred."

Phred didn't say anything, so I said, "I guess he's shy, Mom, but he sure is smart. He was telling me all about Mark Twain, I mean Samuel Clemens."

Mom gave me one of those smiles that said she didn't believe a word I was saying, but thought it was cute. "That's nice, dear. Have you finished your chores?"

"Yes, Mom," I said.

"Good, well you enjoy Phred's company while I start dinner," and with that she walked back into the house.

I gave Phred a real hard look and said, "Why didn't you say something? You made me look like a fool!"

"Maybe I didn't have anything to say. Besides, I came to talk to you, not the whole neighborhood," said Phred.

"Well, okay, but next time you're going to make me look foolish, warn me first, please," I said politely, and from that day on Phred and I spent a great deal of time together.

Chapter Two

"Phred, why are you here?" I asked. It had been a month since Phred first spoke with me on the porch, and I had become used to talking to him as though he were a person. Every day after school we would walk along the creek or borrow my Dad's skiff and explore the nearby marshes together. Phred was excellent company and it had been an incredible month. I could tell he liked it best when we explored the marshes. Phred sat in the bow of the boat while I sat in the stern steering our way through the narrow channels with a small outboard engine. One day he had implied that the wind in his face brought back many an adventure. When I asked him to tell me about some of his adventures he smiled and said, "Oh, just other adventures with old friends, John. Nothing very interesting." I didn't believe him, but decided not to press him. Phred was a mystery. I got the impression he had been around humans a long time, and knew a lot about us. But, mystery or not, I was glad to have him as my friend.

"I told you why I'm here, John, the first day. Remember, I said you looked lonely," Phred replied to my question.

"Oh," I said. "That day I got the feeling you were lonely too."

"There is some truth to that," he murmured. "John, let me ask you a question. As you grow up, what kind of person do you want to be?"

"I don't know," I answered. We were both quiet then. The motor purred away and sea gulls gulled off in the distance. After a few minutes of silence I said, "I suppose a happy person." But even as I said this I thought it was a stupid answer to Phred's question.

"Exactly!" yelled Phred. "Good answer, but I'm curious, why didn't you say a rich or famous person?"

"I don't know." I shrugged my shoulders, still a little amazed Phred liked my answer. "If being rich made me happy, then I would like to be rich and famous too."

"Ah, sometimes it does, but being rich or famous is not the key to happiness," said Phred, matter-of-factly.

"What is, then?" I asked curiously.

This time it was Phred's turn to be quiet. Finally, in the most serious voice I have ever heard him use, he said,

"The key to happiness is discovering your true purpose in life and then following it."

"And how do I do that?" I asked.

"Well, first thing you do is unlearn everything that has been taught to you since you were born."

"Why?"

Phred just stared at me with his serious look. After a moment he said, "Look, have you ever thought about how strange life really is? Before you were born you had everything! A warm, comforting womb to hang out in, food, and the love of another human being. But with the coming of that first slap on your rear end, life became a struggle. We all (meaning people, of course, but for the record this applies to parrots too) had to learn how to cry in order to be fed and changed, but even then we were still happy and content by just being who we were, living in the moment with simple, clear needs that someone who loved us supplied. Our purpose in life was clear: to grow and explore this strange new world we had entered, while being cared for by a family who loved us.

"Then, after a year or two, our parents begin to instruct us how to be good, and for the first time we are subjected to another person's standard of how to behave and live. It is at this point we begin to lose who we truly are and begin to learn to be what other people want us to be. No longer are we allowed to be happy by just being ourselves."

My God, that was the most serious thing Phred had ever said. And though I was still confused, there was a part of me that understood. But before I could say anything he continued.

"Let me give you an example. I once watched a child named Kevin building a sand castle on a beach. I could tell that Kevin was totally into building this castle. His imagination was obviously flowing, and, for the moment, his world was a happy one because his purpose in life was to build this castle. Kevin's mother was reading a book next to him. She was engrossed in the book, but at one point looked up, noticed Kevin building the sand castle, and said, "Why are you playing alone? Go down the beach and play with the other children." Kevin tried to explain he was building a great castle and did not want to play with the other children right now, but all the mother saw was the child being alone. She told Kevin, quite strongly, to go play with the other children, so he sadly left the sand castle and went to play with the children.

"This is a sad story Phred," said John.

"Yeas it is but with an important point," replied Phred. He then continued, "All through our childhood we are given directions regarding what will make us happy. These directions are given to us in a way that, too often, does not take our own feelings and ideas into consideration. The mother did not see her child happily involved in building his sand castle. It's more likely all she saw was her child playing alone and remembered her own loneliness as a child. Because she did not want her son to experience the same pain, she indirectly told him that to be happy you must play with others, and that being alone and doing what you want is not good for you. Unfortunately, most of us have had similar experiences as children, leading us to grow up accepting what our parents and society think our purpose in life is, and not allowing us to find our true purpose. Our parents raise us all doing the best they knew how. Just as their parents did before them. They all want the best for their children and to keep them from the pains of life, and consequently taught them not to explore what their true purpose in life might be, but to accept what their parents and society thought they should do."

"Does this happen to all of us?" I asked.

"Most of us," said Phred.

"I feel like I truly am who I want to be most of the time, but am I, Phred?" I asked.

Phred looked at me and smiled. "Only you can truly answer that question, John, but personally I believe you are your true self," responded Phred. "In fact, it doesn't take a lot when you're a child to learn how keep your true self. All it takes is for someone to love you for who you are and not who you want or hope they will be."

"Oh," I said, but Phred could tell I was still confused.

"Remember the child building the sand castle? Well, sitting with the child and mother was the child's grandfather. After the mother told her son to go play with the other children the grandfather tried to protest on the child's behalf. The mother ignored the grandfather's advice. But before the child left his sand castle he looked up at his grandfather and the grandfather said, "It's a beautiful sand castle." That's all it takes, John, someone who loves you and accepts you for who you are! I suspect your mom or dad or someone else let you know early on that they loved you for who you are."

"Wow, Phred, that story was incredible. I hope everyone has a grandfather who loves them or someone like him."

"Unfortunately, the child's grandfather and people like him are in the minority," said Phred. "Most of us had experiences like the child who wasn't allowed to be himself building the sand castle, and, there wasn't someone else there to tell us how beautiful our sand castles were. But let's not be too hard on our parents. They raised us all doing the best they knew how. Just as their parents did before them."

Up until now I kind-of took my parents for granted. They were just there, and I figured one set of parents was no different from the next. Now, listening to Phred, I began to have more respect for them. They really do let me be whoever I want, I thought. Neither of them ever tried to push me into something I did not want to do, and they were always happy with the grades I brought home. Mom always said as long as I was doing my best that was all that mattered. Dad asked me once if I wanted to go out for the swimming team, since I swam well - he said, 'like a fish.' But I said I didn't, and he didn't seem to mind at all. Mom said if a person enjoys competition they should compete against themself to do better. Mom, at times, is the wiser of the two of them.

After a few moments Phred continued. "John, there is one more important piece to the puzzle of being truly happy."

"What's that?" asked John.

> *"True, deep happiness is not found by looking*
> *for it. True, deep happiness comes to you when*
> *your true self finds its purpose in life."*

"And how do I figure out what my purpose in life is?"

"By growing, exploring who you are, and learning about yourself and the world. Your great American poet and author Ralph Waldo Emerson once said to me:

*'The purpose of life is not to be happy. It is to
be useful, to be honorable, to be compassionate,
to have it make a difference that you have lived
and lived well.' - Ralph Waldo Emerson*

"But for now it is important to understand that people who spend their lives looking for happiness never find it."

"I get it, Phred, deep happiness is kind-of like a byproduct of finding your purpose in life."

"Correct," said Phred, "but an important byproduct!"

Now, the sun was setting in the west. The rays reflected off the water and into the clouds making the horizon look like a beautiful painting.

"Life is good, Phred," I said, and he nodded his head.

Chapter Three

With Phred around the days passed more quickly than ever, and every day was adventure for us. He was full of knowledge. For instance, when we explored the creek he would tell me about the different creatures that called the creek their home. Then, other days, we would climb the strange trees that bordered the creek and Phred would show me birds' nests, explaining what kind of bird lived there and how they build their nests. I decided Phred knew just about everything, though when I told him this he specifically said every teacher is a learner too.

One day after school I had to run errands for Dad, so Phred and I rode my bicycle into town. Phred sat in the basket on the handle bars, and people smiled as we rode by. I guess they weren't used to seeing a parrot riding on a bicycle.

Our first stop was my dad's insurance agent. I was to drop off the hotel's quarterly payment and wait for a receipt. Mr. Ryan, my dad's insurance agent, had a storefront office, and I could see him working at his desk through the window. Phred decided to wait on the bike, so I went in alone.

Mr. Ryan didn't notice me come in until I was almost next to his desk. "Yes, what is it," asked Mr. Ryan without looking up from his desk.

"Good afternoon sir," I replied. "I came in to give you this check from my dad, John West."

"Well, why didn't he just mail it in like everyone else?" said Mr. Ryan.

He seemed annoyed I was in his office, which was beginning to make me uncomfortable.

"Doesn't he realize how busy I am?"

"I don't know, sir," thinking, *why is he asking me what my father thinks?*

"All right, all right, give it over," said Mr. Ryan.

I handed him the envelope with the check inside. "My Dad told me to ask for a receipt with the date on it."

"The man sends his payment in on the day it's due via an annoying little boy and he also wants a receipt. Amazing."

He said this while looking in his desk. I figured he was looking for the receipt book, and didn't really expect me to respond to his statement. Besides, I did not think I was being annoying.

"Here it is with today's date so we both know he wasn't late. Next time tell him to mail it in a few days earlier."

"Yes sir," I answered, and got out of there fast.

John went outside and climbed onto his bike without saying a word.

"Everything okay?" asked Phred, as they rode down Main Street away from Mr. Ryan's office.

"I don't think that man liked me," I replied.

"Well then that's his loss," said Phred. "I could see through the window he looked busy."

"Yeah, he let me know how busy he is," I said, a little hurt by the comment Mr. Ryan made about me being annoying.

"Don't let it worry you, John. You were cool, and you accomplished what you set out to do. Mr. Ryan probably never had a grandfather to let him know it was okay to be himself."

"He definitely didn't seem very happy, Phred," I said. I thought for a moment and asked, "Phred, so how do people find their purpose in life, and happiness, if they have no grandfather like the little boy had?"

"Good question, John. One might think people are doomed for the rest of their lives to be unhappy, trying to find purpose and happiness by someone else's rules. But there is a way to find out who a person really is."

"How?" I asked.

"To begin to accomplish this, we first have to rid ourselves of all the things we were taught we needed to be happy," said Phred. "And the way to do this is by unlearning all the things we thought we were taught. Take a moment and think, what are all the things you believe you must have in order to be happy? If we weren't riding I'd ask you to write them down, and then take a good look at the list. What you would be looking at is all the things your parents, teachers, and society have taught you we need.

Bottom line is we don't need any of those things. The secret to happiness is not obtaining the things on the list, but, as I have already said, knowing who you truly are and discovering your purpose in life. I know, your next question is, how do we accomplish this?" He hesitated, then began, "Well, first, let me explain how most people live today, and then what our options are."

Phred had my complete attention.

"Essentially, most people have been taught to see the world through four different kinds of glasses," began Phred.

I interrupted, "What kind of glasses?"

"John, think about this – how does the world look with sunglasses on?"

"Darker, I guess."

"Right," replied Phred. "Now, how does the world look with amber sunglasses on?"

"Sort-of yellow," I answered.

"Again, right," said Phred. "Well, because we were taught what it means to be good by others, it is the same as having them make us put on a pair of sunglasses. The difference is, instead of seeing the world darker or yellow, we now see the world in the way they taught us to see it. Let me explain the first way we are taught to see the world.

"The first kind of glasses we are taught to wear I call security glasses. Out of the four kinds of glasses, security glasses are the most common pair people wear. With security glasses on people believe the only way to be happy is by having a secure way of living. These people stay in the same job years after the job is no longer enjoyable. They never try to grow or take chances because they are afraid to live life to the fullest. The security of a paycheck or the security of the known is the most important thing in the world to them. They never venture out to live a dream or find their true purpose in life. Being secure is everything for these people, and they teach their children to wear the same glasses."

"Phred, maybe it's because I'm only fourteen, but I hope no one ever teaches me to wear security glasses."

"Don't worry, John, you won't. But, certainly, as with all the glasses we are taught to see life through, there is a problem. In the case of security glasses, no matter how secure people think they are it's all an illusion. ***The reality is, there isn't any security in life, outside the*** *security of knowing who you are, being that person to the best of your ability, and continuing growing and learning your entire life.* Every day we see people lose their job after twenty years, or come down with cancer after being entirely healthy all their life. Yet we are taught to think we can be secure, and that is an impossibility.

Chapter Four

Our next stop was the town department store. Dad needed some stationery for his office. This time Phred sat on my shoulder and came in with me. I knew with other people around Phred wouldn't talk to me, so we walked through the store in silence. As we passed the televisions and stereos Phred whispered, "Nice stereo equipment."

"Sh... Phred, be quiet," I said. We bought the stationery and started home. "Okay, what's the next kind of glasses people are taught to wear?"

"I call them yuppie glasses," he said. "With these glasses on, people are preoccupied with owning material goods. They think by spending all their time working towards owning more and more material goods, they will be happy. In the 1980s a majority of young people called "yuppies" wore these glasses, hence the name, yuppie glasses. It was crazy John, because with these glasses on you believe the only way to find happiness is through buying things. Shopping is the favorite pastime for people like this.

"Not just young people are like this, either. Many people work fourteen-to fifteen-hour days so their children can have cars, stereos, et cetera. Unfortunately, what the children really need is their parents' time and love encouraging them to be themselves. But somewhere along the way these parents were taught that to love their children meant giving them things, and they teach their children the same values."

"Wow, Phred, and people really think that by buying something they will be happy?" I asked.

"Absolutely, and it does work for a short period of time. Of course, it's not the kind of happiness people feel who don't wear any of the four glasses, but for a moment, usually until they bring whatever they bought home, these people are happy."

"I wonder if Mr. Ryan sees life through these glasses. Dad once told me Mr. Ryan works all the time and his family owns a big house, one of those big motorboats we see going out the inlet, and three cars. Yet, even with all that, he didn't seem happy to me."

"I wouldn't be surprised, John, if his parents or someone else told him when he was still a child that the way to be happy was to work hard so he could have all those things," said Phred.

Chapter Five

Reaching home I went to find Dad to give him his stationery and receipt. Dad and Mom had come to like Phred, though they still didn't know how smart he was or even that he could talk. I think they liked Phred because he kept me company and they could see how happy I was to have a friend. But as much as they liked him, he still wasn't allowed inside the hotel. Dad felt the hotel guests might think having a bird loose in the hotel was unsanitary. So while I went to find my father, Phred flew out to the tiki bar.

"Hi Dad," I said, as I walked into his small office. He was adding up receipts on an adding machine, but I knew he would take time to talk with me. I once overheard a hotel guest say my father was the best hotel manager they knew because he was never too busy to talk with his guests. I could have told this person that my father enjoys talking with everyone he meets, and especially with his family.

"Hi son, how was your ride to town?" he asked, looking up from the adding machine.

"Great, Phred enjoyed himself too," I replied.

He smiled and said, "That's nice, John, did you accomplish what I had asked?"

"Yes sir," and I gave him the stationery and receipt. "Dad, is Mr. Ryan happy?"

"I don't know, son, why do you ask?"

"He didn't seem very happy to me." I decided not to mention he also didn't seem to like me.

"Well, maybe he wasn't happy when you saw him. Mike Ryan works very hard and puts in a lot of hours, but he does own a thirty-eight foot cruiser," Dad replied.

"But does owning a big boat make you happy?" I asked.

"It would make me happy, but I'm not sure it makes him happy, especially since he hardly uses it." Dad then got quiet as Phred sometimes does. By now I had learned that when someone gets this way in the middle of a conversation they are usually thinking, and it's best to let them think. So, while Dad stared off into space, I wondered what Phred was doing out at the tiki bar. Finally Dad said, "John, Mr. Ryan has everything a man could want, but doesn't really appreciate it. Consequently, I agree with you, I don't believe he is very happy. Remember, John, "It's better to have a few things and appreciate them, than a lot of things and not appreciate any of them."

"Especially when you're being your true self," I added.

Dad looked at me and I thought he was going into another thinking mode, but after only a moment he said, "Yes, that's right."

"Well, I have to go. Phred's waiting for me out at the tiki bar. See you later, Dad."

"Bye son, I'll see you for dinner."

Chapter Six

P hred was sitting in his usual corner at the end of the bar, listening to the tourists partying it up at the other end. I could see the tourists must have come off the yacht tied to the dock. There were half a dozen of them, all young and tanned.

"Hi Phred," I said, as I walked along the bar, passing the tourists.

"Hi John," said Phred using a squeaky voice people usually hear from parrots.

"Hey, the parrot talks," cried one of the tourists. "Polly want a cracker?" said another.

"No, Polly doesn't want a cracker," I said, thinking another jerk vacationing in Florida.

The tourist looked at me and Phred, laughed, and turned back to his friends. "Forget them, Phred, they're jerks," I said when I reached Phred's end of the bar.

Between the loud, obnoxious tourists and the music from the bar radio, the bar was fairly noisy. No one would hear Phred and me talking, and we faced looking out at the bay so they wouldn't see us talking either.

"Phred, what kind of glasses are those jerks over there wearing?" I asked, pointing at the tourists.

"Those young people were taught to see life through glasses I call pleasure glasses. With these glasses on, everyone is always looking for pleasurable experiences. In other words, these people are always looking for amusing things to do, believing if they spend all their time doing fun things they will be happy," said Phred. "You see people wearing these glasses every winter here in the Florida Keys. They come down from the north to party."

"All those people, Phred, are only happy when they're here?" I asked.

"No, not all, but a good many of them. Especially the ones who have jobs they don't like but they keep them because their salaries mean they can afford to go out and do fun things. I know a lot of this sounds strange to you, John, but you haven't been in a corporate office, and I hope you never are. There are a lot of unhappy people working in jobs they don't like so they can party on the weekend and go on vacations."

I looked over at the tourists almost with a sense of pity. "You know, Phred, you're painting a pretty ugly picture of life as a grown-up," I said.

"I know that, but it is pretty ugly out there for an awful lot of people. And you haven't even heard the last kind of glasses people wear. In some ways they're the worst of the four, but enough for to-day. I'll tell you about the fourth pair of glasses some other time, and about the lucky people who don't wear any glasses at all."

Several weeks went by and we didn't talk about people or the glasses they wear. Phred knew I needed time to digest what he had already told me. I didn't realize it at the time, but because of these conversations with Phred I was beginning to grow up.

Chapter Seven

It was an easy Saturday afternoon and Phred and I were fishing off Point Key. Several sailboats could be seen a mile off towards the setting sun. We had cut under the bridge that connected the Keys and were on the western side. The fishing was supposed to be better on this side, but we really didn't care. Phred and I came out here just to be on the water. Seeing for miles around always made me feel free. For Phred I think he enjoyed the wind and air. Off in the distance I could see a Navy jet cutting a path through the sky.

"Phred, do you see the jet over there?" I said, as I pointed to it.

"Yeah, I see it," said Phred.

"The jet is beautiful, but why do we need a military?" I asked.

"So we can defend ourselves against bad people," said Phred with just a little hint in his voice that told me he wasn't being completely serious.

"What bad people?" I asked.

"John, there are always people who want to dominate other people, even in our country."

"Are they wearing a special kind of glasses?"

"I call them power glasses because these people are into the kind of power that helps them dominate other people. You see, John, these people are preoccupied with dominating people and manipulating situations. People wearing this kind of glasses make excellent politicians, corporate employees, or ladder climbers. Increasing their wealth, prestige, pride, and power over people is important to them. But, like all the other glasses, none of them truly make anyone happy."

"But isn't that the way of the world?" asked John. "Darwinism, survival of the fittest, and all that stuff? Isn't someone dominating someone else part of our biological makeup?"

"Yes, that's what you were taught in school, and as far as most human beings are concerned survival of the fittest is the most important law of nature thereby making it a scientific fact of life or, even more, a universal truth that all living creatures follow." Phred paused for a moment and then continued, "Consequently, if survival of the fittest is a universal truth that all living creatures follow, then humans had better be the ones on top dominating and controlling everything, including each other," said Phred.

"Exactly!" exclaimed John. "If humans are just playing out a universal truth then how can they be wearing glasses?"

"Because survival of the fittest is not a universal truth. It's an assumption, or what some people call "a mental model," that you humans believe is a universal truth, but it is not," answered Phred.

"But Darwinism proved it is," said John.

"No, Darwin observed this phenomenon in nature, and over time society decided that this phenomenon, or law of nature, existed everywhere so it must be a universal truth. What Darwin didn't observe is that nature also has species living in symbiotic relationships. This means there are many species that cannot get along without each other, which is another law of nature. For example, it is a biological fact that ants cannot exist without bees. Both species need each other to survive. And there are many examples like this in nature."

"So survival of the fittest is not a universal truth for all species," said John.

"Correct," said Phred. "It is just one phenomenon in nature, along with many other phenomena in nature, and is not the only way living creatures live in the world!"

"Well then why do people think survival of the fittest is a universal truth?" asked John.

"Because over time Darwin's observations became, in human's minds, the only laws of nature that they observed. If he had observed nature's symbiotic relationships, of which there are many, then instead of people believing 'survival of the fittest is the only law of nature,' people today might believe instead that 'sharing and being cooperative is the only law of nature.'"

"Wait a second, Phred, so what you are saying is that laws of nature are not absolutes pertaining to all living creatures."

"Correct, what they are are phenomena that consistently occur in nature. The issue for humans is that you observe a phenomenon, decide it's a fact for all living creatures, then create a universal truth like 'survival of the fittest is what living creatures follow,' and then everyone, meaning you humans, believes this and acts according to this so-called universal truth. And the even stranger part about all this is most humans believe and act on these so-called 'universal truths' from an unconscious level, meaning they are not even aware that they are acting out their lives based on truths that are not universal at all. And which may even be unhealthy for themselves and others."

"Wow, Phred, that is a lot to take in," said John.

"Okay, let's see if I can explain this better. Humans, like other thinking species – parrots for example – observe the world around them and develop as a society, mostly unconsciously, what some people might call universal truths that are not universal at all, but are really just something I, and others, call mental models. *Mental models are unconscious assumptions or rules society teaches us about how the world works, which we then act on.* For example, if we believe 'survival of the fittest' is a fact of life, or the only law of nature, then wearing power glasses would seem like a good idea."

"Yeah, that makes sense," replied John. "All these things are going on inside our heads, mostly unconsciously, meaning without us being aware that we think this way, and then we act out our lives based on these assumptions or rules."

"Exactly, it is just like the story of one fish saying to another fish, 'The water is really nice today.' And the other fish says, 'What water?'"

"I get it!" exclaimed John. "It would be like me saying to someone, 'This mental model really makes me believe the world is…' whatever I think the world is. Fish don't realize they are swimming around in water, and humans don't realize we are living out our lives following certain mental models we were taught, probably starting at a young age."

"True, John, not only are humans unaware that they are living their lives by mental models they were taught starting as children," said Phred, "but they are not even aware that they have mental models. And, if you try to make them aware of them, they will say, 'Well those are just facts or universal truths, and, being facts or truths, they cannot be changed, so I should live my life by them.'"

"But they are not universal truths!" exclaimed John.

"Again, exactly," said Phred. "And because they are only mental models, we need to first be aware of what they are and how they make us act, and, second, decide 'is this the way we want to live?' This brings me to one of the key principles to finding your true purpose in life, and that is:

> *'the key to discovering your true purpose in*
> *life is understanding your mental models*
> *and changing the unhealthy ones'.*

"And how do I do that?" asked John.

"By observing how you think," answered Phred.

"Huh?" said John.

"What we need to do is watch our thinking and say to ourselves, 'why do I think this way?' And, 'what are the mental models behind why I think this way, and how do I act out these mental models in my day-to-day living?' People that learn to do this learn to not wear any glasses at all, and begin to see the world as it truly is."

Chapter Eight

"Okay Phred, tell me about these people who don't wear any glasses at all," I pleaded.

"Well, people who don't wear any glasses are people who understand that being their true self and finding their purpose in life is the key to being happy. In other words, only people who do not wear any glasses can discover their true self, find their purpose in life, and, as a byproduct, find happiness. These people spend time observing, thinking, and reflecting about what their mental models are, and learning to change the ones they don't think are healthy. They also enjoy taking on new challenges to help them discover what they like to do, what they don't enjoy doing, and who they connect with in order to help them discover what is their purpose in life. This action-observation-reflection-action process is a lifelong journey."

"Wait a second, Phred. Are you saying it takes your entire life to discover who you are and your purpose in life?" asked John.

"No, not your entire life," said Phred. "But it is a journey. Children do this naturally, and as long as adults encourage children to continue to think, learn, and take on new challenges, children will do this their entire lives. Unfortunately, most parents are already wearing one of the different kinds of glasses and teach their children to do the same. But your question is does it take your entire life to discover who you are and find your purpose, and, again, the answer is no. If adults don't teach you otherwise, such as by teaching you to see the world through different kinds of glasses, by the time you reach adulthood you will have a good idea of who you are and what is your purpose in life."

"So why do you say you need to do this your entire life?'

"Because adults change as they reach different ages, and losing your way is not uncommon."

"Okay, I think I am following you, but let's start with at what age does one become an adult?"

"It depends on the person. Some people never grow up and act like children their whole lives. But, for argument's sake, let's say children become adults when they support themselves with food, shelter, and clothing. That's when adulthood begins."

"Wow, I have a ways to go," replied John.

"Yes, you do, but, again, it's not about getting somewhere, it's about the journey. And, even more important, it's about knowing the importance of and gaining the skills of learning how to think, learn, and take on new challenges, even in childhood."

"Okay, but, again, once we learn how to discover who we are and what our purpose in life is, how do we then lose ourselves?" asked John.

"Because who we are at twenty-five is not who we are at thirty-five or forty-five, and our purpose in life may change. Consequently, learning how to think for yourself, continuing learning about who you are, what are your mental models, what is important to you, who is important to you, and what is your connection or relationship with them, and then turning this observing, thinking, reflecting, and learning into new actions that are challenging and support your growth is all very important in achieving a happy and satisfying life."

"Again, wow! You sure give me a lot to think about, but it also sounds very worthwhile. Thanks, Phred."

Chapter Nine

John and Phred spent the next several days fishing and enjoying being on the water after school was over. One late afternoon after sharing John's snack on the skiff, John rebaited his hook and then said to Phred, "Phred, I am doing my best to remind myself that life is about seeing the world as it truly is by understanding what my mental models are, but how do I find my true purpose in life?"

"Obviously, John, each person must discover for themself what their true purpose is, but I can tell you another key characteristic to all true purposes." John became real quiet so Phred could tell he had John's complete attention. "Another key principle:

a true purpose is always about being part of something greater than yourself that makes the world a better place for more than just you.

"Material goods and pleasurable activities are secondary to being part of something greater than yourself. For example, people that do not wear glasses also take the time to understand and connect with the people around them, and the more they connect the more they see themself in everyone they meet, and vice versa. By doing this they begin to see themself and everyone as full human beings with strengths, weaknesses, fears, etc."

"It sounds complicated, Phred," I said, a little confused.

"Not really, John, but it is a life-long journey."

"But Phred, how can you be so sure you're being your true self?" asked John.

"You might not always know for sure. But you do the best you can and enjoy the day," answered Phred. "People who do not wear glasses are experiencing life to the best of their ability each day. Let me tell you a story that was told to me by Art Buckwell, the famous columnist. It is about a person who doesn't wear any glasses. This is how he decided to be his true self, to be part of something greater than himself and connect to others…

(Art Buckwell) *I was once in New York riding in a taxi with a friend. When we got out my friend said to the driver, "Thank you for the ride. You did a superb job of driving."*

The taxi driver was stunned for a second. Then he said: "Are you a wise guy or something?"

"No, my dear man, and I'm not putting you on. I admire the way you keep cool in heavy traffic."

"Yeah," the driver said and drove off.

"What was that all about?" I asked.

"I am trying to bring love back to New York," he said. "I believe it's the only thing that can save the city."

"How can one man save New York?"

"It's not one man. I believe I have made the taxi driver's day. Suppose he has 20 fares. He's going to be nice to those twenty fares because someone was nice to him. Those fares in turn will be kinder to their employees or shop-keepers or waiters or even their own families. Eventually the goodwill could spread to at least 1,000 people. Now that isn't bad, is it?"

"But you're depending on that taxi driver to pass your goodwill to others."

"I'm not depending on it," my friend said. "I'm aware that the system isn't foolproof so I might deal with 10 different people today. If, out of 10, I can make three happy, then eventually I can indirectly influence the attitudes of 3,000 more."

"It sounds good on paper," I admitted, "but I'm not sure it works in practice."

"Nothing is lost if it doesn't. I didn't take any of my time to tell that man he was doing a good job. He neither received a larger tip nor a smaller tip. If it fell on deaf ears, so what? Tomorrow there will be another taxi driver whom I can try to make happy."

"You're some kind of a nut," I said.

"That shows you how cynical you have become. I have made a study of this. The thing that seems to be lacking, besides money of course, for our postal employees, is that no one tells people who work for the post office what a good job they're doing."

"But they're not doing a good job."

"They're not doing a good job because they feel no one cares if they do or not. Why shouldn't someone say a kind word to them?"

We were walking past a structure in the process of being built and passed five workmen eating their lunch. My friend stopped. "That's a magnificent job you men have done. It must be difficult and dangerous work."

The five men eyed my friend suspiciously.

"When will it be finished?"

"June," a man grunted.

"Ah. That really is impressive. You must all be very proud."

We walked away. I said to him, "I haven't seen anyone like you since 'The Man from La Mancha.'"

"When those men digest my words, they will feel better for it. Somehow the city will benefit from their happiness."

"But you can't do this all alone!" I protested. "You're just one man."

"The most important thing is not to get discouraged. Making people in the city become kind again is not an easy job, but if I can enlist other people in my campaign..."

The sun had set and the stars had started to come out. I didn't respond to Phred's story. I didn't think he expected me to, but he gave me plenty to think about.

Chapter Ten

Summer vacation had arrived, and being out of school meant I had more time to spend with Phred. I didn't know it then, but Phred was teaching me more about the world and life than anyone ever taught me in school. One of the nicest things about Phred was he could pick right up on a conversation we had several days or weeks before, like no time had passed at all. Phred was not only teaching me, but he had an immeasurable amount of patience with me, too.

"You know, Phred, the way you talk it sounds like the whole world is made up of people trying to be happy but not succeeding because they are trying to be happy in all the wrong ways," I said, a little depressed. We had been fishing for a couple of hours, and fishing always gives me the time to think.

Phred didn't respond immediately, so I concentrated on the fishing. After a while he said, "I believe I'm giving you a distorted picture of the world, John. Let me back up for a moment. First, most human beings in the world are poor. I'm not sure what the percentages are, but most of the human race lives in poor countries. For these people life is a daily struggle. Finding food, shelter, and clothing, and working towards a better future for themselves and their families takes up all their time and energy. If they can accomplish this, many of these people are truly happy. Ironically, they know life is difficult, but they also know they are part of something greater than themselves, and, remember, this is the key to knowing one's purpose in life. This is true for many of the poor people who live in America too. So remember, John, when I talk about the people who have been taught to wear different kinds of glasses, I'm not talking about the poor, many of whom already have their true purpose in life, but the privileged few."

"But who are these privileged few?" I asked.

"John, the privileged few are people who will always find food, shelter, and clothing, and, consequently, have the choice of making their life whatever they are willing to try for. For better or worse, these few are the adults and children of the middle, upper, and wealthy class in all the countries of the world. We see a lot of these people because America has such a large middle class."

"Why do you say 'children' of the middle, upper, and wealthy class?"

"Because in order for someone to believe that food, shelter, and clothing will always be there, they have to have felt that since birth. I won't say it is something parents teach their children, but it is something that children of these classes feel early on, even if they don't realize it. This is a funny phenomenon, John, especially for the new middle class in America."

"'New middle class,' what's that?" I asked, realizing I was asking a lot of questions this afternoon.

"The middle class in America is relatively new, or at least the size of it is new. America always had a middle class, but it wasn't until after World War II that it grew to such a large size in this country. Have you ever heard an elderly person talk about the Great Depression?"

"Sure," I said.

"Well, the people who went through the Great Depression knew what it was like to be poor and hungry. After the Depression their dream in life was for their children never to feel hunger. For many, their dream came true. The 1950s and '60s America prospered. People bought houses in suburbia and moved their families into them. It is the children from suburbia and their children that learned to wear these special kinds of glasses. Of course, the wealthy were already wearing them."

"Putting it the way you just said, Phred, I would think the people who are poor are the lucky ones," I said, trying to make it sound like a joke.

"I can see why it might look that way, John, but being poor is no fun. The middle and upper classes have everything: choices, opportunities, and food, shelter, and clothing. They may not choose well, or realize how lucky they really are, having never experienced being poor, but they do have all the advantages. The poor do not."

"I hear you, Phred. Sorry I made a joke out of it," I said. "Tell me more about why Americans have learned to wear different kinds of glasses."

"All right," said Phred. "The second half of the twentieth century is a time when Americans can say, 'America has made it.' As I have already said, a prosperity has been reached where many have obtained the basics of life: food, shelter, and clothing. Very few times in history can a society say they have had these three basics for a large portion of the population. On the other hand, John, because 'America has made it,' many people, especially the middle and upper-middle class, have a new problem and that is: now that America has made it, where does it go from here, or what do individuals and a nation strive for? The answer many chose is, 'to strive for more and more material things.' More cars, more televisions, more goods. Much of the reason America chose this way is because of the glasses Americans have been taught to wear. Now, I realize that now, at the beginning of the 1990s, Americans do not have as much as they did in the 1950s or 1960s but we still can say, 'American's have made it.' Americans have more. For the middle class it used to be Americans wanted 'a chicken in every pot.' Today it's, 'if I see chicken once more this week I'll scream.'

"Phred, this sounds to me like another Catch-22," I said.

"It is, John. You would think, 'America has more, so then why are Americans still not satisfied?' The answer is the glasses Americans wear to see the world through. Wearing any of the different kinds of glasses makes Americans believe

> *'it is not what they have or do that determines whether*
> *they think they are doing well,*
> *but it is whether they have or do more -*
> *more than their parents,*
> *more than ten years ago, etc'.*

"Be it more security, fun, material possessions, or power, they have to have more. I call this, John,

> *"the never enough syndrome."*

"Remember the people who wear the yuppie glasses? They're a good example of the never-enough syndrome. Most of these young people were raised with a relatively affluent childhood, consequently, they have to have more than what they grew up with. But, because of the never-enough syndrome, no matter how much such a person achieves they will not be satisfied.

"Another reason this 'more and more' material growth is a hollow achievement I once heard characterized by an sociologist Dr. Paul Wactell in his description of the modern man: 'The modern, affluent man drinks Brazilian coffee, smokes a Cuban cigar, sips good brandy, while reading the N.Y. Times, all at the same time, with varying degrees of success.' John, Americans don't appreciate what Americans have because

> *'they have so much and they don't*
> *take the time to appreciate it'''.*

"You know, Phred, my father said something very much like that the other day about Mr. Ryan not really enjoying the things he owns."

"Good example, John, and Mr. Ryan's children probably have no time to play with the toys that fill their closets, because there are always new ones to be played with. Yes, America has achieved more, but at the price of its own happiness and contentment! It is a crazy world, John. People buy material goods thinking this will bring them happiness. They also buy things because, at least in part, they are unsure of how to use their leisure time. Making a purchase is time-consuming, and this makes shopping one of Americans' favorite pastimes."

"I'm beginning to understand, so that's why so many of my schoolmates spend so much time at malls," I said, realizing it's a funny world I live in, and I have a great deal to learn before I understand it.

Phred agreed with me and then said, "There are two other important issues with America's 'more and more' society. The first is how all this affects the earth's resources. With the coming of the agricultural and industrial age humans have learned to dominate nature. This domination has grown as our production of goods has grown, and if America keeps putting economic growth first, it will sooner or later run out of the earth's resources. The second issue, John, is America uses over thirty-five percent of the world's resources, while having only five percent of the world's population. If it keeps using a large portion of the world's resources and resources become scarcer, how will this affect the rest of the people on the earth? Consequently, I don't want to be a doomsayer, because we can change, but at the moment our environment is also at risk, along with Americans' personal happiness and contentment. As I said, it's a crazy world."

"What you're saying, Phred, is, since buying material things will never make us happy, and it is also using up the world's resources, then we must change, right?"

"You got it, Johnnyboy!" said Phred. "Remember, John, most of the world is still struggling for food, shelter, and clothing, so we're really only talking about a small population of the privileged few."

"The middle and upper classes," I answered.

"Right, and these middle and upper classes might be the majority in America and other rich nations, but they're also in poor nations, just not as many of them."

"Darn, Phred, that's still a lot of people!"

"True, but something else I have noticed over the years is that much of the world tends to follow America in their changing values. In other words, if America moved away from materialism to something better, chances are the rest of the world would move with it."

"So all you and I have to do is change America!" I said sarcastically.

"Yeah, John, that's all," said Phred calmly.

"Phred I know you're smart and I know I'm just a kid, but even I know two people – or one person and a parrot – can't change the world." Saying this I figured that was the end of this conversation. I was wrong.

"Oh yeah, do names like Gandhi or Einstein mean anything to you? John, a great anthropologist named Margaret Mead said it best when she said,

> 'Never doubt that a small group of thoughtful,
> committed citizens can change the world.
> Indeed, it's the only thing that ever has.'

"And don't forget, John, the key to a true purpose in life is always about being part of something greater than yourself that makes the world a better place for more than just you. Can you think of any greater purpose to be part of than supporting a better way to live?"

"Okay, I concede your point, but Phred, I'm no Gandhi."

"Why not? You're only fourteen. How do you know you won't grow up to be another Gandhi? Do you think Gandhi knew at the age of fourteen what he was going to become? But even more to the point, Gandhi was just one person; he needed supporters to accomplish what he accomplished. America needs leaders with a better vision in mind for America than just materialism, but it also needs people who believe in that vision.

"Another thing, it's been shown by examining humankind's past that changes in a society take on a life of their own when five to fifteen percent of the society accept the new change. It's kind-of like a snow-ball rolling down a snowy hill. It takes a small amount of work to start the snowball rolling, but once it's rolling the ball rolls by itself, getting bigger and bigger. Changes in society only take a small percentage of the society to accept and embrace the change before it takes on a life of its own. So you see, John, Gandhi only needed a small percentage of his society to accept his ideas. Once this happened it was only a matter of time before his society as a whole accepted his ideas as their own."

"You win, Phred. I believe you, and as you already said,

'a true purpose in life is always about being part of something greater than yourself that makes the world a better place for more than just you.'"

"Very good, John," replied Phred.

"But what kind of change would we want for America?" I asked.

"John, I can tell you my ideas, but you're pretty smart, so what would yours be?"

"Okay, let me think. First off, forget about endless materialism. We already know it doesn't make anyone happy for very long. Oh, I still think Americans should have things, but they should keep it to a reasonable limit and appreciate and care for what they do have. It's wrong that we have five percent of the world population, and use over thirty-five percent of the world's resources. Maybe if we used less, others could have more and there would be fewer people strug-gling for food, shelter, and clothing.

"Good, what else?" asked Phred.

"Next, I want people to take off those stupid glasses, learn to understand their own mental models, then change the ones that are unhealthy and enjoy life for what it is. As you said weeks ago, life is a journey with highs and lows, similar to the way a river flows. I'd like to tell people that life is a journey to discover what it means to be part of something greater than themselves that makes the world better off."

"Not bad, John, you have been listening and thinking," ex-claimed Phred.

"Thank you. You give me a lot to think about."

"What else would you like to see changed?"

"Well, I agree with you that people will be happier if they realize they are wearing distorted glasses that make them see the world defectively. If only they realized that they have been wearing these glasses, took them off, and began the journey of finding their true purpose in life! You know, Phred, what I'm saying isn't all that difficult. To change takes mindful discipline and an awareness of the world around you but it is possible."

"That's very true, John! I wish more people would just try!!!"

PART TWO

CHANGING THE WORLD

Chapter Eleven

Except during the summer months, school kept John occupied every day till three o'clock. John liked school for the most part, but felt for some reason he was learning more from Phred than he did from most of his teachers. Phred once commented to John that some schools up North were experimenting with year-round schooling. Both of them found this idea appalling. Those summer months were special for both of them. John explained how on the first day of summer vacation he always had a feeling of freedom and excitement. Knowing he had the whole summer in front of him would always bring feelings of an adventure about to begin.

On the other hand, school wasn't too bad. There was always something new to learn. John learned particularly well from his science teacher Mr. Clemens. Mr. Clemens taught his students by having them participate in class projects. One such project which appealed to John was one where the class had to do something to help the environment. Most of the children chose recycling at home as their project. Each student put several boxes or shopping bags somewhere in their kitchen and labeled them in order to save bottles, cans and newspapers. John had already been doing this. He started recycling soon after Phred had discussed the never-enough syndrome with him. John needed another idea, so, of course, he discussed his problem with Phred.

"Phred, remember I told you how Mr. Clemens gave our class an environmental project assignment in honor of the coming Earth Day activities?"

"Of course, John, I always enjoy hearing about Mr. Clemens' assignments. He is one of your smarter teachers."

"Yeah, well, most of the other kids are starting a recycling proj-ect at home, but, as you know, I already did this. Consequently, I need a new idea. Any ideas?"

"Many, John, but aren't you the one who should come up with the idea?"

"Yes, but I'm kind-of stumped. I want to do something new."

"Okay, maybe I can get you started. Talking about Earth Day does remind me of one of the unfortunate outgrowths since the yearly Earth Day celebration began in 1970. This outgrowth is the false idea that individual recycling can alone save our planet. Now, don't get me wrong, individual recycling is a good thing and, what's more, it is helping you humans change the mental model that 'throwing things away is okay because the earth has unlimited resources and plenty of room for humans' garbage,' to 'the earth has limited resources and way too much garbage.' Unfortunately, individual home recycling is only part of the solution."

"I know, Phred, we also need to quit thinking that buying every-thing in sight will make us happy."

"Right, John, but there is something else that needs to be done. Earth Day helped put the focus of attention on preserving our planet through individual activity. This in itself is a positive step forward, but many businesses have supported this idea because it has taken the attention away from them and things they could be doing to protect our environment. The bottom line is that, in order to save our planet, big business also must change to recycling programs for the products they produce and the waste they make in producing these products."

"Okay, but how can they do this?" asked John.

"A first step could be for corporations to begin asking them-selves the question 'how do we change from using basic raw materi-als for production of a product and their excess waste, to using basic raw materials plus the recycling of old products for the production of our product with little or no waste?' Recycling of newspapers to make more paper is an example of using an old product to make a new product. A good example of a person who thought ecologically is a woman named Sally Fox."

"Hold it, what does 'ecologically' mean?" asked John.

"Thinking ecologically means subscribing to the idea that every-thing on this planet is interconnected. The word 'ecology' is from the Greek word 'oikos' meaning 'household.' The word in English means 'the study of earth household,' or, more precisely, it is the study of relationships that interlink all members of the earth household.

"Anyway, back to Sally Fox. Cotton is one of our most chemically polluting crops in the world. It is being grown on two percent of the world's land, but it receives twenty-six percent of all the pesticides used in the world."

"That's a lot!" blurted John.

"Yeah, it is. Sally Fox knew this and began thinking, 'how can we preserve our planet and still produce cotton for the making of clothes?' I wouldn't be surprised if Sally had a parrot for a friend, but no matter how she came up with the idea of saving the planet and producing ecology-based cotton is not important. The point is she did. When Sally started her company, Natural Cotton Colors, Inc., she decided she would produce cottons without pesticides, chemicals, bleaches, and other toxins. Through experimentation Sally produced naturally colored cotton. This means, John, no chemicals for the dying of cotton. Her naturally-grown color cottons were different shades of brown, mint green and even pale pink. On an ecologically-based foundation, she alone is slowly changing the cotton industry. Right now her chemical-free cottons are more expensive than chemically-grown cotton, but if more people bought her cottons, her prices could become as cheap as chemically-grown dyed ones.

"And, remember, it all started with the desire to address this problem," explained Phred.

"In other words, Phred," John stated, "Along with the saying,

> *'Never doubt that a small group of thoughtful,*
> *committed citizens can change the world.*
> *Indeed, it's the only thing that ever has,'*

we can also say,

> *'If a small group of committed citizens can change the*
> *world,*
> *then one person willing to be the catalyst to begin to*
> *motivate the small group can begin that change.'*

"Sally Fox is one example," continued John.

"Sure, you could say that. There you go, John that can be your environmental project."

"What could be my project?" replied John.

"You can be a catalyst to motivate people, maybe your fellow classmates, to changing the world?" answered Phred.

"Yeah right, Phred, as soon as I become president of the United States."

"Not a fun job, John, and besides, the American people want a hero for their president and what they get are mere human beings. But I'm serious, John, pick a project, something that the world will be better off if you can make it happen."

"Again, Phred, like what, and remember, I'm just a kid."

"Your brain is already in a defeatist mode. Believe in yourself, John. Think of something around here you don't think is good for you or other people."

"Something around here I don't think is good?" John pondered aloud, "Well, there is that old cement factory. You know, the old factory we passed in the boat. The beach around it is littered with junk, and the water is always dirty. Almost like something is spilling into it."

"Good, I agree, I don't like that place either. Reminds me of too many places like that that I've seen in my travels," responded Phred.

"But what could I do?" asked John.

"To start, find out what is spilling into the water. Go get a clean jar from your Mom. We'll go over there now, get a sample of the water and then ask Mr. Clemens where can you send it to get it analyzed."

"You know, Phred that might work. I could also probably find out in the library when the factory closed, and maybe even who owns it."

"Excellent, John, and, remember, factories give off waste. If you can find out what kind of waste products cement factories produce we might be able to investigate if any of those waste products are still around on the grounds."

"Okay, Phred, I don't know if I can motivate anyone to help change the world, but I like this as a science project."

Chapter Twelve

The next day John came home from school all excited. "Phred, Mr. Clemens took the jar and said he would give it to the Health Department for analyzing. Also, five other students asked if they could investigate this problem with me."

"Wow, John, it looks like you might have the beginning of a small group. What did the six of you decide to do next?"

"Well, we met after class and divided into three groups. Two of us are going to research possible hazardous waste from cement factories, and two others are going to try and find out who owns the property now. The last two are investigating what environmental laws protect our community."

"Sounds good," said Phred.

A week went by. John and his classmates did their research. They discovered the property was owned by a Miami-based corporation. They also discovered that some of the waste products from a cement factory are definitely harmful. After three phone calls to the corporation they finally reached someone who said there were no hazardous materials left on the site after the factory closed. John was not so sure this person was speaking the truth. For one, the person who finally answered their question was from the corporation's public relations department. Two, he answered the question without doing any research. The idea that he knew this information off the top of his head seemed unlikely. John believed the person knew he was speaking to a kid. And, finally, upon investigating the factory grounds, John and his classmates found some old rusted barrels leaking whatever they had in them.

"Phred, we have all this information now, but what can we do about it?" asked John.

"Brainstorm solutions, John. Between the six of you I'm sure you can come up with something," answered Phred.

"Maybe, but the project is due next week. We're not going to have a solution by then."

"All right, advertise!" exclaimed Phred.

"Advertise what?" asked John.

"Advertise the information you have. Make a poster showing what you learned. At the bottom of the poster give a date for a meeting to explore solutions. Invite anyone who is interested."

"That might work. The poster could be our class project. We could take a picture of the rusted barrels we saw, and then describe what the public relations man said."

"Also, put in some of the environmental laws you found in the library," suggested Phred.

"Okay, Phred, I will see if I can sell this idea to the others in my group."

"John, when you talk to them, leave room to incorporate their ideas too."

"Sure, Phred. No problem."

Chapter Thirteen

Two weeks later Phred was hanging out at the tiki bar waiting for John to come home from school.

"Hey, Phred," said John as he walked up to Phred. "Man, did I have a tough day in school."

"Well, I'm glad your home, John. Why don't you grab a coke from the cooler and tell me about your day." Coming home from school and telling Phred about his day had become a ritual for them. Phred sometimes told John about his day too, but, more often, John wanted to tell Phred about something that happened to him and then ask Phred to explain something he didn't understand or was confused about. Ever since John began his environmental project, their talks became more and more important to both of them.

"Okay, Phred, but you won't believe what I'm about to tell you."

"Try me," said Phred, as John pulled out a coke and popped the top.

John took a sip of the cold coke, remarked the cold coke was just what he needed, and launched into his story. "Well, you remember my environmental exhibit. We made that poster about the problem of possible hazardous waste out at the old cement factory. At the top of the poster we printed the saying:

> *Never doubt that a small group of thoughtful,*
> *committed citizens can change the world. Indeed,*
> *it's the only thing that ever has.* - Margaret Mead

"And at the bottom we invited other classmates to join us, setting the meeting date for tomorrow after school. The poster was hung up on the wall outside of Mr. Clemens' class where my history teacher saw it. Anyway, at the beginning of history class Mr. Pike, he's my history teacher, asked me in front of the whole class to give him an example of when a small group of people ever changed the world? But before I had a chance to respond he said, 'And don't give us that nonsense about environmental groups making corporations clean up their pollution.' Well, Phred, that stopped me dead in my tracks. I started to ask him, 'what's wrong with environmental groups?' But before I could even say that, he cut me off and told the class that the only thing that ever changed the world is large armies conquering little armies. He finishes by saying only idealistic fools think they can change the world. Of course that cracks the whole class up because he is obviously trashing me. What a jerk."

"Sounds like a real nice guy, NOT!" joked Phred. "Did he ever give you a chance to talk?"

"No, after the class stopped laughing, he went right into his lesson. I've got to tell you, Phred, I felt a little stupid."

"Sure, you got set up by a real jerk. Even worse, this jerk, being a teacher, used what I call power-over against you. Did you consider getting up and leaving?"

"Yeah, right, and end up in detention too? That would make me feel very stupid!"

"Good old power-over right at work," answered Phred.

"Besides, I could tell many of the students bought into Mr. Pike's ideas because he's the teacher."

"Adultism," said Phred.

"What, Adult... what? And, power-over?" John responded.

"One word at a time. Adultism, not a word many people know, but almost everyone has experienced it."

"Okay, what is it?"

"Adultism is the oppression of children by adults These adults have their power glasses on." Phred paused for a moment and then continued, saying, "The essence of adultism is that a young person is disrespected by an adult. You see, the mental model people have is: 'young people are not smart enough to learn for themselves and must be told what to learn.' This leads to adults automatically believing they know what is best for children. Children cannot be trusted to learn correctly, so they must be taught, disciplined, punished, or harnessed (which is what your history teacher was doing to you), and guided into adulthood."

"I certainly did not feel respected by my history teacher."

"Did you also feel controlled?" asked Phred.

"Yeah, I did. He has the power to give me detention. Is that power-over?"

"Yes, but he also controlled you by making fun of you. It was made even worse by doing it in front of other people. He harassed you, John, until your spirit was broken, and that is how he controlled you. People do this to each other all the time, and especially adults to children. Think about comments adults use all the time such as, 'Oh, it's only puppy love,' or 'What do you know? You're just a kid.' Comments like these are telling children their feelings and knowledge are somehow inferior to those of adults."

"But why do they do this, Phred?" asked John.

"The simple answer is people unconsciously believe in the mental model that young people are not smart enough to learn for themselves and so must be told what to learn."

"And what's the complex answer?"

"The complex answer is because they're being oppressed too. First as children, and then as adults. Our society is packed with institutions, such as schools, or customs that are oppressive in nature. All through life there is always someone in authority telling someone else what to do, think, or feel."

"But isn't that the way of the world?" asked John.

"For most, yes, but who's to say it has to be that way? I thought Americans prided themselves on having freedom to choose? Well, if they do, then why can't you all choose not to believe in the mental model that people are not smart enough to learn for themselves and must be told what to think, feel, and do?

"I don't know, but I bet you have an idea."

"Maybe. For one, people don't know that they were taught the mental model 'people are not smart enough to learn for themselves and must be told what to think, feel, and do,' but I also think it's easier for people to allow someone else to make decisions for them. This way they can blame someone else besides themselves if things go wrong. Another reason is because many people think, like you said, this is the way of the world. But what these people don't realize is the fulfillment that comes from making one's own decisions."

"It's learning time again, Phred. I grasp most of what you are saying, but please explain slowly," said John with a slightly confused expression on his face.

After a pause Phred continued, "You see, John, oppression has two forms: external and internal. External oppression is what happens when adultism is put into action. How often does an adult let a child gift-wrap a present?"

"Gee, Phred, my mom always let me wrap the presents even when I was small. Of course my wrapping wasn't very good."

"Exactly, maybe your wrapping wasn't very good, but let me ask you two questions. One, did you know at the time your wrapping wasn't perfect? And two, how did you feel about wrapping the present?"

"I can remember being very happy giving dad his birthday present wrapped by me, and, no, at the time I thought the wrapping was perfect."

"Now, how do you think it would feel if, instead of letting you wrap your father's present, your mom said she would wrap dad's present because you would make a mess?"

"Not very good," mumbled John.

"That's adultism in action. Your mother, without meaning to, would have made you feel inferior. By not letting you wrap the present she would have been exerting power-over and that's external oppression."

Phred's ideas always made John think.

"Now, external oppression leads to internal oppression. Internal oppression, in this case, would be the feeling by the child that the adult must be right, which could consequently cause the child to learn to have a negative feeling about themself. For example, if your mom had said she would wrap the present because you would make a mess, your personal feeling might become, 'I am no good at wrapping presents and my mom is.' By adults making a child feel inferior, they're supporting the child in believing that the child is not as good or as important as an adult. Obviously, the wrapping of a present is not a big thing, but three or four small things like that a day and over a period of time… well, these actions can cause the slow killing of a child's spirit."

"That's not good," acknowledged John.

"No, it isn't good and it continues all through life," said Phred. "As children begin to grow up and go out into the world, adultism and external oppression will be found everywhere. The big one children run right into, head-on, is the idea that 'the teacher knows all,' and children, now students, don't know anything. This disrespect of a student's knowledge, ideas, and feelings leads to internal oppression, and can cause students to assume that the teacher has the right answer and they don't. Even in adulthood, internal oppression continues because of the mental model 'people in authority know better than others' causing a worker to assume that only their superior in the organization knows what should be done next. John, from day one people are taught to allow themselves to be manipulated by external and internal oppression."

"Incredible, Phred."

"The incredible part is that they don't have to belong to these oppressive customs or institutions! By just not. They just can choose not to buy into the mental models the institutions or customs create. If anyone – a person, an institution, or societal custom – tries to oppress you, the simple answer is: just change your mental models. Eleanor Roosevelt, the wife of President Roosevelt, once said, 'No one can make you feel inferior without your consent.' It's that simple, John. Unfortunately, many people have grown to feel inferior because, unconsciously, they are buying into these oppressive institutions' or customs' mental models, and this creates power-over situations."

"Oh yeah, you mentioned power-over before. What exactly is that?" asked John.

"Power-over is the relationship of domination. It's characterized by inequality, competition, hierarchy, and win/lose situations. Our whole society is structured on power-over. It plays itself out in situations in which a person has the ability to control the behavior, thoughts, and values of others in order to fulfill their own desires or wishes. External and internal oppression are very much linked to power-over, but, before I totally bum you out, let me add that it does not have to be this way; there are other ways to live, or other mental models to believe in, that are healthy."

John did not say anything, so Phred continued.

"The alternative is something called power-with. Power-with is the sharing of individual power in group form in order to achieve a common goal. It is used when people see each other as equals, and respect each individual's opinions and values. People that aspire to power-with can shatter power-over structures by agreeing to change the social structures and mental models they live under, and creating a more equitable way of living together."

"That's the way I want to live!" exclaimed John.

"Then that is the way you will live, but it does not come automatically, John, power-with must be learned. Let me ask you a question. When the students who want to help on the environmental project get together, how will you decide what you will do?"

"I don't know. I thought we would just talk about it until we came up with an idea."

"There are many ways to talk, John, and, unfortunately, the way we are used to is to think of an idea, latch onto it, and then argue for this idea."

"Oh, you mean like debate," said John.

"Yes, like debate, but debating too often leads to power-over by one person pushing their ideas and attacking others."

"Oh, Phred, kids would never do that. That's a grown-up thing."

"John, I wish that was true, but I see kids doing it to each other all the time. Just watch a group of kids trying to choose a game to play in the playground. It might start out with no one wanting to make a suggestion, but before the decision is made there is usually an argument."

"Yeah, you're right there, so what is the alternative?" asked John.

"Well, another way to make decisions is by establishing a different set of communication rules. The opposite of a debate is something called dialogue, and there two key differences between debate and dialogue. The first is that debate tries to change the other person's view by attacking any ideas that are not in line with one's own, while dialogue asks the group to share their views from their own individual points of view. The second is that in a debate, when decisions are reached, many times by voting, someone always wins, and someone always loses. Whereas in dialogue common ground is looked for in order to try to create win-win solutions for everyone." Phred paused to see if John was still with him.

"You know, Phred, it sounds to me like debate is for people that follow power-over and dialogue is for people that want to create power-with," said John.

"You got it!" cried Phred. "Now tell me, what are the mental models behind debate and dialogue?"

"Well, let's see, the mental model behind debate is, 'my ideas are better than anyone else's ideas,' and for dialogue the mental model is, 'if I can understand what the other person's ideas are, together we can find a better solution to whatever we are discussing,'" said John.

"Good," said Phred. "You are beginning to get the idea of what mental models are.

"Now one more thing about power-with. Power-with helps create something called power-from-within. And this kind of power, power-from-within, gives us the energy to find our true selves."

"How does it do that?" asked John.

"Well, power-from-within is a feeling inside us that says 'this is right for me,' or 'this is who I am.' It comes from the individual's discovery of their true self. It is very strong! Power-from-within has been described as akin to the 'sense of mastery' little children discover for themselves with each new ability, as they stand erect, take their first steps, and first find the magic of using words to convey their thoughts and needs. As I said, it is very strong and energetic. It can demolish all the hidden feelings of inferiority from internal oppression, and, together with the energy of other people creating power-with, it can shatter power-over and external oppression."

"All I can say is, wow!" exclaimed John in astonishment.

Chapter Fourteen

The next day John and his classmates met after school in the room they had advertised for the meeting. They were hoping other students would come, and were happy to see sixteen additional classmates show up. This brought their strength up to twenty-two. John started by telling everyone what he had learned about the closed factory: that it was owned by a Miami-based corporation, and how the corporation's public relations person had said there were no hazardous materials left on the site, but that he had said this without doing any research which made John and the original five classmates suspect he was just telling them what he thought they wanted to hear and it might be true or not. Finally, he told how Mr. Clemens sent off their jarful of the liquid to the Health Department for analyzing. He then asked if anyone else had any information to add.

A boy in the back said, "Two years ago I got a bad skin rash after exploring in the old factory. The doctor said it was probably from something I touched while exploring."

Another boy said he saw dead fish floating on the beach near the factory. John said he had also seen the dead fish and added, "The beach by the factory is always dirty. It is as if something is leaking into the water."

A new kid asked, "Okay, but what can we do about all this? We're just kids."

"Kids can make a difference!" said George, one of the original five. "It's going to be our world someday."

"Yeah, but what can we do?" asked another person.

"Well, it seems to me that first we have to see if we need to do anything," said another student. "If we need to do anything at all depends on what is spilling out of those old cans."

"Mr. Clemens said the Department of Health should have the analysis of what is spilling out of those cans in a week," John commented.

"Okay, so let the Department of Health handle the situation," said the boy who felt kids couldn't do anything.

Another boy turned to the boy who just spoke and said, "That's stupid! Government people don't do anything."

It was easy to see that, after being called stupid, the first boy's feelings were hurt. This made the other kids uncomfortable. John knew he had do to something or this meeting would be their last, so he cut in, "Hold it, we're getting ahead of ourselves. We know from meeting today that several kids here have seen the pollution and have even been personally affected by it. Let's wait until Mr. Clemens has the analysis back and then meet again."

"Makes sense to me," said one of the original five.

John looked around and it seemed others agreed. "Okay, this meeting is closed. Since we all know each other, we will just contact each other about when the next meeting will be." And, with that said, the kids began to leave.

"How was your meeting after school?" Phred asked when John reached home.

"Okay, I guess," answered John. "Twenty-two kids showed up."

"Twenty-two is good. So why the, 'I guess?'" asked Phred.

"Well the meeting seemed to be going fine until one kid called another kid stupid. And, Phred, the kid was not stupid. He just had a different opinion than the guy who said he was stupid. Besides, where does anyone come off calling someone stupid, especially to their face. Man, it changed the whole meeting."

"Yeah, I can see how calling someone stupid to their face will change the atmosphere in a group of people, but tell me exactly what they disagreed about."

"Well, one boy said we should leave the problem of the pollution at the old factory to the government officials, and then the other boy said he was stupid to think government people will do anything."

Phred grinned a little and said shyly, "Well, maybe the boy is right and the other kid is stupid."

"Phred!" John exclaimed.

"Okay, okay, I apologize. At least I didn't say it to the boy's face, and of course I never would. And there are good people in government who would do something if they thought they could, but the question is, are you and your group going to leave it up to the government to fix this problem?"

"I don't know, we never got that far in the meeting. I ended the meeting before the bad atmosphere could get worse and make it so no one would want to come back. I said I would call another meeting as soon as Mr. Clemens had the results of the test back."

"Wow, the atmosphere was that bad, huh? Then it was good you did end the meeting."

"Yeah, but what am I going to do now? I'm not even sure I can get the kids to come to another meeting."

"Oh, there are definitely things to be done. But first, let's figure out why what happened happened."

"That's easy, the guy who called the other boy stupid is a jerk! And, no, I wouldn't say that to his face either."

"Okay, this guy's a jerk. By the way, what is this jerk's name?"

"Bill, and the boy he called stupid was Bob. I know them both slightly."

"Okay, what kind of power relationship was Bill trying to create - and it looks like he succeeded - with Bob?"

John thought for a few seconds and said, "Well, it sure wasn't power with! It had to be power over." He thought some more. "Yeah, definitely power over."

"He succeeded, too, didn't he," said Phred. "He backed Bob up and probably hurt Bob's feelings."

"Oh, yeah, that was plain to see by everyone," said John.

"He hurt Bob's feelings, made Bob unsure of himself, and, at the same time, strengthened his own conviction that he was right, creating a power-over relationship. There was a good chance if the meeting had continued that Bob would have talked more, and probably louder. Bill would have been silent and you would have lost him after this meeting. So now you're going to have to do some damage control in order not to lose him."

"Makes sense, but what?" asked John.

Phred was quiet for a minute. Then he said, "There's going to be a pretty sunset in a couple of hours. Why don't you change, clean up, and meet me down on the pier to watch it. We'll talk some more then." John nodded his head and went to change.

John joined Phred at the end of the pier just before the sun touched the horizon. "I made it," said John as he sat down on the last plank of the pier. Phred was standing on one of the last pilings looking out at the sun.

"You know, John, I have been watching sunsets for a long time now and they always center my spirit. Humans should watch more sunsets. Okay, where did we leave off?"

"You were telling me that now I would have to work to get the boy who was called stupid to come to the next meeting. I understand what you mean, but what can I do?" asked John.

"Remember when we talked about external and internal oppression?"

"Sure, I remember. It comes from people who buy into power-over relationships."

"Exactly," said Phred. "And you witnessed power-over between those two boys. Do you remember what needs to be done to combat power-over?"

"Something about power-from-within," answered John, a little unsure.

"Again, correct," answered Phred. "Power-from-within is that feeling inside us that says 'this is right for me' or 'this is who I am,' and it demolishes all the hidden feelings of inferiority that come from internal oppression. Your job is to help the boy Bob find his power-from-within."

"Wait, I got it!" exclaimed John. "What you're saying, Phred, is that when the boy called Bob stupid he was creating a power-over situation of 'you're stupid and I'm not.' And, by Bob buying into being called stupid, Bob was allowing internal oppression to be created: 'He's right, I am stupid.'"

"Very good so far," said Phred. "Now, where does power-from-within come in?"

"Since Bob has bought into the idea that maybe he is stupid, or at least his ideas are stupid, he needs to tap into his power-from-within which will tell him, 'No, I'm not stupid, nor are my ideas. In fact my ideas are as good as anyone else's.'"

"And how can he do this?" asked Phred with an expression that told John he was right.

John paused for a while and was silent. It was clear his mind was thinking hard. The final tip of the sun could be seen falling behind the horizon. "By me talking to him. But not by me telling him 'you are not stupid.' No, that wouldn't work. Bob has to decide for himself that he and his ideas are okay. This means I have to help Bob decide that for himself."

"Good!" exclaimed Phred. "Now you know what your job is."

"Yeah, but how do I help Bob make that decision?" asked John.

"The same way I help you. By asking the right questions! I once heard Mark Twain say, and I believe he was quoting Socrates,

> *People will learn:*
> *- 20% of what they hear*
> *- 40% of what they hear and see*
> *- 80% of what they discover for themselves.*

"Okay Phred, but I still don't know what I'm going to ask him," said John, a little unsure of himself.

"It will come to you," answered Phred.

"I hope so, but what about this next meeting after we get the results back? How do I prevent the same thing happening again?"

"Create a dialogue," answered Phred simply.

"Create a dialogue," murmured John under his breath. "And what, pray tell, is a dialogue?" But before Phred could say anything John added, "You know, Phred, this is all pretty complicated."

"True, my friend, and not true. It's true what I am suggesting is complicated because people are not used to doing what I am suggesting to you. It's not true because what I am suggesting is simple once people learn how to do it. People are not taught dialogue, people have been taught debate. And changing the world means changing the way people communicate." Phred paused. "How much of this are you following?"

"Not a whole lot. I do get the idea that the world is not in the greatest shape. You and I have talked about this. But I don't understand this idea of a new way of communicating. What's wrong with how we communicate?"

"Nothing, if you enjoy debating and it's important for you to win all the time while someone else loses. As long as people communicate that way the world is going to stay a mess."

"What you're saying is the communication of debate creates a win-lose situation, and you know that also creates a power-over relationship."

"You got it! Now explain to me what the communication of dialogue will create?" asked Phred, happy with John's response.

"Well for one, it would have to create a power-with relationship and a win-win situation. I understand what dialogue can do, but, Phred, I still don't know what it is."

Phred thought for a moment, while darkness fell around them. They had been so engrossed in their conversation that they hadn't noticed the sun had gone completely down and it was dark on the pier. "I'll tell you what, John, it's late and we should go in. After all, it's a school day tomorrow. What I will do is type out the difference between debate and dialogue on your computer. After that we will talk some more."

"Okay Phred, we should get in," replied John.

That night while John slept, Phred pecked away on John's keyboard, so in the morning the screen showed the following diagram:

Difference Between Debate and Dialogue for small group work.

DEBATE
- Participants listen in order to refute the other side's data and to expose faulty logic in their arguments.
- Participants usually speak as representatives of groups.
- Statements are predictable and offer little new information.
- Debates operate within the constraints of mainstream society.

DIALOGUE
- Participants listen to understand and gain insight into the beliefs and concerns of the others.
- Participants speak as individuals.
- New information surfaces or new knowledge is created.
- Participants are encouraged to question mainstream society's ideas and look for alternatives.

Phred was asleep when John woke up, so John read the diagram to himself. Below the diagram Phred had also written the following:

There are three key differences between debate and dialogue. They are: one, debate tries to change the other person's view by attacking any ideas that are not in line with their own. Conversely, dialogue asks the members of the group to share their views from their own individual point of view. Attacking another person's viewpoint is not part of dialogue. The second major difference is that dialogue will lead to new information or the creation of new knowledge. Debate usually offers little to no new information or knowledge. Finally, in debate, when decisions are reached, many times by voting, someone always wins, and someone always loses. Whereas in dialogue, common ground is looked for in order to try to create win-win solutions for everyone. Simply put, in debate people push their own ideas doing little or no listening to others' ideas, while in dialogue people spend the time trying to understand others' ideas, values, and beliefs.

"Man, Phred is good," thought John. Without waking Phred up, John dressed and left for school.

Chapter Fifteen

John caught up to Bob walking home after school.

"Hi Bob, thanks for coming to the meeting the other day," John said, starting the conversation.

Bob looked at John suspiciously. "Yeah, sure," answered Bob.

"I'm thinking of calling a meeting next Wednesday. Mr. Clemens said the results should be back by then." Bob didn't respond so John continued. "I hope you can make it."

"Maybe," replied Bob and they were both quiet.

After about five minutes of the two boys walking in silence, John finally said, "Hey listen, I thought Bill was wrong in calling you stupid."

"It doesn't matter," answered Bob.

John thought, "Man, he's not making this easy." Then he said out loud, "No, I mean it, Bill was wrong and I promise it will not happen again."

"How can you stop it?" asked Bob.

"By setting down some ground rules before the meeting. Like, all ideas are worthwhile," answered John.

"Do you really think that will stop people like Bill from trashing everyone's ideas?"

"To be honest, no, not at first at least, but I will also say I am going to monitor the ground rules, so the first time he does say something negative, I'll call him on it. He still might not stop immediately, but if others support me, he will."

"That does sound all right, John, but why do you want me anyway? I really don't have a lot to offer."

"Sure you do, Bob. Aren't you willing to put some time and energy into doing something about that old factory?"

"Yeah, if there really is something I can do."

"Why?" asked John.

"Why what?" replied Bob.

"Why are you willing to try and do something about that old factory?"

"Well, I don't know, because it's ugly and I really think it is hurting us. I've seen those dead fish washed up on the beach."

"Good, Bob, the fact that you care is why we need you at this meeting."

Bob thought for a little and then said, "All right, I'll be there."

"Thanks, Bob, my home is this way," said John, pointing down a side road. "I will let you know when the next meeting is."

"Okay, see ya, John." And both boys walked off in different directions.

The next day John came running home to see Phred. He had already narrated to Phred all the details of his encounter with John the day before. Phred told him he did real good. Now John came running onto the dock panting, "Hey Phred, we got the report! And, boy, were we right!"

"So, tell me," replied Phred.

They flipped through the pages together. The report indicated that harmful chemicals, solvents, and other metals had polluted the ground and surrounding water. It listed pollutants such as copper, lead, zinc, and others John and Phred had not heard of. "Wow," said Phred, "it's worse than I thought."

"Yeah," answered John. "What can we do about all this?"

"Good question. I look forward to hearing what you and your group come up with."

John called a meeting for Friday afternoon after school. Twenty out of twenty-two showed up. Bob and Bill were there.

"Before I show everyone this report we need to first establish some ground rules," said John starting the meeting.

"Why?" asked Bill, sarcastically.

Another boy asked, "What are ground rules, John?"

"Ground rules are how we are going to treat each other in these meetings. For instance, when someone has an idea it will be against the rules to trash it."

"But that's no fun," said a boy, looking at Bill and smiling.

Someone from the back of the room said, "Trashing someone else's ideas is not the way to have fun."

Several other kids nodded their heads in agreement. John and Bob crossed eyes, both thinking that maybe others felt the way they did.

"But how will we decide anything if we do not debate each until we agree on doing something?" asked Bob with a little less authority in his voice.

"By creating a dialogue," answered John.

"What's dialogue?" another kid asked.

"A dialogue is a different way of communicating. It is actually the opposite of debate," said John. "Here, I made a flipchart of what dialogue is and how it is the opposite of debating." After saying this, John went over to the wall and pulled up a map. Underneath the map was Phred's chart of the difference between debate and dialogue for small group work.

DEBATE
- Participants listen in order to refute the other side's data and to expose faulty logic in their arguments.
- Participants usually speak as representatives of groups.
- Statements are predictable and offer little new information.
- Debates operate within the constraints of mainstream society.

DIALOGUE
- Participants listen to understand and gain insight into the beliefs and concerns of the others.
- Participants speak as individuals.
- New information surfaces or new knowledge is created.
- Participants are encouraged to question mainstream society's ideas and look for alternatives.

Below this outline the following was written:

Essentially, there are three key differences between debate and dialogue:

(1) Debate tries to change the other person's view by attacking any ideas that are not in line with their own. Dialogue asks the group to share their views from their own individual points of view. Attacking another person's viewpoint is not part of dialogue.

(2) Dialogue will lead to new information or the creation of new knowledge. Debate usually offers little to no new information or knowledge.

(3) In debate, when decisions are reached, many times by voting, someone always wins, and someone always loses. Whereas in dialogue, common ground is looked for in order to try to create win-win solutions for everyone.

The last flipchart showed the following statement:

In debate people push their own ideas doing little or no listening to others' ideas, while in dialogue people spend the time trying to understand others' ideas, values, and beliefs.

The room was quiet while everyone read the chart. Many of the students were nodding their heads while reading. Finally, Bob said, "Those ideas work for me. I like them." Several other students said the same.

"Okay, they're interesting ideas, but I don't see how they are going to work. Grown-ups can't even follow those ideas," commented Bill. "And how will we make decisions?"

John had explored this exact question with Phred the night before. "That is not 100% true that all adults do not dialogue. Elders in Africa dialogue when discussing important decisions. They use something called the talking stick." John then pulled a small piece of driftwood out of his pack. The driftwood, about ten inches long, fairly straight and round with only a slight twist in it, looked like it once belonged to an old sailing ship. "Okay. What the African elders did was pass the stick around to the person who wants to speak. Only the person who holds the stick can talk. While this person talks, everyone else's job is to listen. When they are finished then someone else may ask for the stick and talk. What we are looking for is common ground among the speakers and, hopefully, for an answer to emerge that everyone can get behind. If this doesn't happen, we look for an answer that everyone can live with."

Another student said, "In other words, consensus. But isn't consensus alone very time-consuming? And now, with the introduction of your talking stick, even more time-consuming"

"Yes, it is," replied John, "but, one, by taking the time I honestly believe there is a good chance a better idea will emerge. And, two, once we have the idea, if we have all agreed upon it, then hopefully this will create energy in each of us to get behind it and make it happen." Creating power-from-within and power-with said John to himself.

Bob immediately jumped in, emphasizing, "And if we debate, someone has to lose, and most likely they will have little energy for the idea that won."

"And that's why we're here! We have to do things different than the adults or the world is never going to change." Everyone turned to the person who said this. It was a girl named Kate.

"Kate's right," said John. "Everywhere I look I see grown-ups trying to establish power over each other. That's what debating is really all about. Someone always wins, while someone else always loses. What we need to do is create our group differently."

"Exactly," stammered Kate. "We need to be a group where not one person is the boss, telling us what to do. We each must strive to treat each other as equals. Like this chart says, we must each listen to each other's point of view and look for common ground." John and Kate crossed eyes. It was clear to both of them that they thought alike.

"What Kate is talking about has a name, it's called power-with. Power-with is the sharing of individual power in groups in order to achieve a common goal. It is used when people see each other as equals and respect each individual's opinions and values."

Most of the students were nodding their heads. This told John that the group agreed with Kate and him. Since no else seemed to want to talk he said, "Okay, I think we are ready for the report." With this said he pulled the report out of his school bag. John handed the report to the kid sitting next to him. He and two others started skimming the report. When they reached the part about harmful chemicals, solvents, and other metals polluting the ground and surrounding water they read it out loud to everyone.

After a brief silence Bob said, "We were right, it is dangerous."

"Wow," exclaimed someone from the back of the room. "We were right. The place is a dangerous place."

"Do you think we will all get cancer?" asked another. John thought he must be thinking about all the problems they had in New England with chemical pollution.

"Hold on, everyone. Time to use the talking stick," said John, holding up the piece of driftwood. A girl named Jessie raised her hand and John handed her the stick.

"We don't know," she said, "and proving that these chemicals cause cancer in our town is very difficult. But that does not mean they don't, and we need to do something about it."

"But what?" asked Bob, and then said, "Oops, may I please have the stick"? He raised his hand and Jessie handed him the stick. "What can we do? We are just a bunch of kids."

John raised his hand and Bob handed him the stick.

"Wait we are getting ahead of ourselves," said John. "First, do we all agree this report says there is something bad going on out at the old factory?"

"Yeah," said several others, and one of these kids asked for the stick.

"But now that we know this, what can we do about it?" he voiced.

John asked for the stick. "Let's put the talking stick down for a minute and just brainstorm some ideas," said John, and walked up to the blackboard. "Remember, in brainstorming there are no bad ideas."

Someone immediately said, "We need to know more about these harmful chemicals. I suggest we go to the library and learn more." John wrote on the blackboard: 'Research harmful chemicals.'

Then someone else said, "I think we should show this report to the newspaper." John wrote down: 'Go to newspaper.'

"Okay, so we go to the newspaper and maybe they do an article, but we need to do more. I think we should picket outside the old factory," said another student.

"Yeah, and start a signature campaign demanding the company remove these bad chemicals," said another.

"With the signature campaign we can also find out how many people know that there are harmful chemicals right in our community," voiced Kate.

Meanwhile, John was writing all this down on the blackboard.

While students were calling out their ideas, other students began to talk excitedly to each other. John observed this and thought this is what Phred meant by the creation of power-with. Once the brainstorming seemed to be over with, John said, "Okay, raise your hand if you want to work on one of these ideas. I will call out each idea."

The students raised their hands as John spoke out each idea. At the end there were about four or five students willing to work on: (1)

Finding more information on the harmful chemicals; (2) Going to the local newspaper; (3) Finding out how to start a signature campaign.

John closed the meeting with, "Since Friday afternoon seems to work for all of us, let's meet next Friday. In the meantime, meet with the group you signed up for and move forward with your assignments. We will start the next meeting with updates from each group."

The groups worked hard over the next week, charged by a feeling that this was their mission, not just an assignment given to them by a teacher. John told Phred that almost every member of the group had come to him personally over the course of the week to relate to him their fears and hopes. Fear that some adult would sooner or later stop their mission, or that after all their work nothing would happen, and, yet, hope that they could do something worthwhile, make a change in the world to something better.

On Friday everyone showed up for the meeting, but before it began John reminded everyone that they were to practice dialogue communication, not debate. This time no one protested and most students were nodding their heads.

"Okay, let's see where we are," John began. "Group one, have you discovered anything new about the chemicals at the site?" A tall, skinny kid raised his hand and John gave him the talking stick.

The tall, skinny kid said, "It seems almost all those chemicals listed in the report cause cancer if you are exposed to them in large quantities. The problem is no one knows for sure how much is meant by 'large quantities.' What we can say is that those chemicals are seeping down into our drinking water."

"Good work," said John, taking back the stick. "Now let's hear from group two."

A girl named Violet stood up, took the stick out of John's hand, and said, "I decided to join this group because my dad knows Mr. Johnson, editor of the town's local weekly. So our group went to Mr. Johnson at his office on Wednesday, and he said that if harmful chemicals are leaking into the town's drinking water then he would be willing to write an article about it."

"Wow," exclaimed two boys sitting behind Violet. "We need to get this information to Mr. Johnson," said another student, but then he quieted down because he realized he did not have the stick.

John was smiling because he could see that the group was getting excited. He took the stick from Violet.

"Before we decide what is next let's hear from the third group. I am in that group, but, Bob, why don't you tell them what we learned," He handed Bob the stick.

Bob stood up, a little nervous, and began, "John, Pam, and I went to the library and did a search on signature campaigns. It seems a group of kids in Kansas got their town to stop spraying pesticides along the highway because the pesticides are also harmful chemicals to humans."

A girl next to Bob took the stick out of his hand and said, "If they are harmful to people, why are they being used?"

Bob politely took the stick back and said, "Well, the town officials said that, for one, this has been the way they have always kept the bushes from growing into the road. And they also said that, in their professional opinion, the amount of pesticide they sprayed was not harmful."

"Yeah right," said the boy behind Violet sarcastically. It was Bill again. "Then how come most of the people I know that died, died from cancer?" As soon as he finished talking he realized he did not have the talking stick, and John could see on his face he was embarrassed. This was the first time he had spoken up in the group since he and John had had that confrontation several weeks ago.

"Just because it's always been done that way doesn't mean it's a good way. I'm getting real tired of people telling me 'the world is going to hell in a hand basket, and nothing can be done about it,' or 'don't worry, science will solve our problems.' Hell, it's science that got us into these problems in the first place!" exclaimed Bob.

"My dad's a doctor, and are you trying to tell me that medical science is not good? My dad works very hard helping people get well!" exclaimed another girl named Mary.

"No, I don't mean that," defended Bob. "What I mean is..."

But Bob stopped to gather his thoughts, and before he continued John interrupted and said, "Stop, we are starting to do it again!"

"Doing what again?" asked Bob, a little put out that he had been interrupted.

"Debating each other," said John. "We agreed to try to be different and use dialogue, so let's back up. Mary, instead of telling us about your dad, ask Bob a question that may give you a deeper understanding of what he is trying to say."

"Okay," said Mary. After thinking for several moments she said, "Bob, I agree with you that we hear all the time that the world is getting worse, and, sure, science has given us a good deal of problems, especially environmentally, but are you saying all science is bad?"

Bob, feeling better that John had asked Mary to try to question him in a respectful way, answered, "Is science all bad? Maybe not all, but it sure has caused us a lot of problems."

"Yes, I agree," said Mary, "but my dad's a doctor, and science has given him some great knowledge to help people get healthy and live better lives."

"Okay," said John. "Medical science has done great things for us, but it's become a science of getting people healthy after they have become sick. What about the science of helping people be and stay healthy?"

Another boy said, "Exactly, I'm happy we have good doctors who can help my Mom beat breast cancer, but my dad said that years ago people did not get cancer as much as they do today. Why is that? And, if we know certain chemicals cause cancer, even if only in large quantities, why do we still use them?"

There was silence in the group. Finally John said, "I think this is what dialogue is supposed to do. Instead of giving us quick answers, it is designed to make us think and look for new answers. Let's continue this dialogue after we all have had time to think. Okay?"

Everyone nodded.

John then said, "Along with thinking, what else do we need to do before our next meeting?"

"I would like to show this report to my dad and his friend Mr. Johnson, the editor of our town's weekly paper," said Violet.

"Okay, Violet, I will make you a copy and give it to you tomorrow in school," replied John.

The next day Violet sat down at John's table in the cafeteria during lunch. "My dad said he would talk to his friend Mr. Johnson and show him the report," began Violet.

"That's great," replied John, and he handed her a copy of the report.

"He also said that Mr. Johnson would ask our congressperson for a response to the report."

"Cool, but why?" asked John.

"My dad said that the government has money to help clean up places that are very polluted."

"Okay, but wouldn't that be the responsibility of the people or company that caused the pollution in the first place?"

"I suppose," replied Violet. "I will ask my Dad that question."

"Thanks, I really appreciate the time you are putting into this project, Violet," said John. They both finished their lunches and, when the bell rang, they moved on to their next class.

John had called a meeting for a week later, but, two days before the meeting, the weekly town newspaper, called The Key Weekly, came out with a headline: "Old Tire Factory Polluting Our Water Supply." In the article were the key points from the report about the different cancer-causing chemicals found in the water. Also written was how this report was part of a middle school class science project. Mr. Clemens was quoted talking about how he encourages his students to do real-life projects. Finally, there was also a quote from the district congressperson, promising to look into this matter.

"Phred, we are doing it!" exclaimed John as they drifted and fished in John's skiff.

"What you have accomplished is pretty impressive, John," said Phred, pleased that John was excited. "What are you going to do in tomorrow's meeting?"

"I thought I would see if the other students wanted to start a signature campaign to make the corporation clean up the mess they left behind?"

"Good idea," replied Phred, and they both fell into silence. The sun was setting in the west and it was another beautiful afternoon on the water. John was sitting in his skiff, peacefully drifting along, not really concentrating on fishing but just letting his mind wander, while Phred was perched on the bow thinking his own thoughts.

"Phred," John said softly, "I still do not understand why we humans are letting the earth go to hell in a hand basket? You know, my dad was telling me the other night that he can remember when they built the tire factory. He was just a small boy, younger then I am today, but he still remembers how excited the whole community was!"

"Did he say why the community was so excited?" asked Phred.

"Yeah, he did. He said the tire company meant jobs. There were not many jobs in the area back then. Before the tire company, then other businesses, and, finally, tourism, came to the Keys, young people that grew up here either became fishermen or left home for a job up in Miami."

"Well, the life of a fisherman is not an easy one, but many people loved that life," said Phred.

"Yeah, I would rather be a fisherman than work in a factory or have to work and live in a city."

"I am with you, John, but many people don't think they have any choices in how they live and work," replied Phred.

"I know we have talked about this, the type of glasses people wear that make them see life in a certain way, but what about those people that loved growing up in the Keys and yet moved to the city for work. You would think they would have been smart enough to have known they already lived in a beautiful place, and even if they didn't know it, living in the city for a while should have helped them appreciate where they came from," John exclaimed.

"Why don't you ask your dad why these people did not become fishermen like their fathers before them?" answered Phred.

"I will," responded John, and, with that said, he pulled in his fishing line and started the outboard for home.

Chapter Sixteen

L ater at dinner, John asked his Dad why people who grew up in the Keys left for jobs in the city.

"Well," said John's father thoughtfully, "many left, and still do, for the excitement of city life. But most left, especially when I was young, because there just weren't enough jobs here for them."

"Why didn't they just become fishermen like their fathers?" asked John.

"Maybe the oldest boy did follow his father to the sea. But this was not enough money for all the siblings to follow their father in their father's occupation. The others had to look elsewhere for work. Also, remember, John, back then families were much larger than they are today."

"That is another thing I don't understand, why did people have so many children?"

John's dad looked at his son the way all parents look at their children when they first realize their children are growing up and are almost adults. "People have had large families since humans have inhabited the earth for three major reasons. One, birth control as we know it did not exist. Two, most humans were farmers, and the more children a family had the more hands they had to work the farm." John's dad thought for a few seconds and continued, "Finally, because we did not have doctors and hospitals, many children died. Families had lots of children because only a few were expected to live into adulthood. But in our modern society that has all changed." With this said, John's dad excused himself and went off to work the evening shift in the hotel.

John did his homework and got ready for bed. Phred sat in his favorite place in John's room, on top of the closet door. After John put on his pajamas he turned to Phred and said, "Phred, did you by any chance hear what my father was saying at dinner?"

"Yeah, I heard him. I was sitting outside on the porch enjoying the evening air. He's right, you know. You humans are taking over the world just by there being too many of you."

"I agree, but how bad is it really?" asked John.

"Well, I seem to recall a graph in your biology book. Look up the word 'population' in the index." John found the graph.

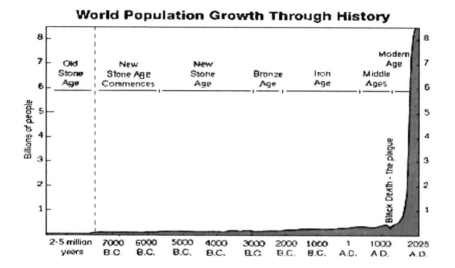

World Population Growth Through History

"Wow," exclaimed John. "Look at the population climb in the last few hundred years! This is amazing!"

"Yeah, it's pretty incredible," whispered Phred. "You humans are the only species ever to produce so many in such a short history span that cover our whole planet, but it cannot continue."

"But, Phred, even with birth control available for many people in the world, we do not seem to be slowing down."

"That's true, John." Phred stared at John for a long moment and then said, "The only known birth control that is known to work for an entire population is economic development. People stop having large families when their income improves enough that they know they are not going to go hungry. America is one of the best examples of people stopping overpopulating the planet once they reached a certain economic level, but there are other examples too. Singapore is an Asian country that in the past had large families, but once Singapore reached a certain economic level, people there stopped having too many children. You see, John, as I said a few days ago, large families were a way for parents to assure themselves that they would be taken care of in their old age. Once people realize that they have enough to survive in their old age, having many children is no longer necessary. Hence, smaller populations."

"Well, the United States is not overpopulating. Ms. Higgins in geography class said that the population growth rate in the U.S.A. is one of the slowest in the world. After all, Phred, we have economic development, and we don't need large families to grow our food, we have machinery to do that."

Phred, who was normally very patient with John, responded a little angry, "Yeah, but even with your slow growth rate you still use over thirty-five percent of the world's resources."

"I didn't mean to say we don't have a lot of people, Phred, just that we are growing slowly," John blurted out.

Phred deliberately slowed his breathing down in order to center himself. He wasn't used to being upset with John, or anyone for that matter. He prided himself on his patience. After a minute of silence he said, "John, the United States uses over thirty-five percent of the world's resources but has only five percent of the world population. Do you think that is fair?"

John, who also was not used to Phred being impatient, replied, "Well, putting it that way, no, it does not seem fair. How can something like that happen?"

"Good question. Basically we are back to power-over. After World War II, and even before the war, the United States had the power (militarily and economically) to say to most of the world, especially the third world countries, 'we will buy your natural resources for peanuts, and pay your labor force peanuts, because we have the power to do this.' John, why do you think a poor Indonesian worker will accept a four-dollar-a-day job making Nike sneakers which you will pay at least seventy-five dollars for?" asked Phred.

"Popular sneakers cost a lot more than seventy-five dollars, Phred," injected John.

"True, but for the example's sake seventy-five dollars is fine," replied Phred.

John was silent for a few seconds and then said, "I don't know, Phred. It doesn't seem fair. Maybe the Indonesian only needs four dollars a day? I seem to remember hearing living in those countries is a lot cheaper than here."

"True, people in third world countries do live simpler lives. Of course, ask them how they would like to live and they will say 'like you,' John. But, even living simpler lives, an Indonesian family cannot live on four dollars a day. It always amazes me how one group of people can push down another group of people without even knowing it. Because I will tell you, John, it has been my experience that most humans are good people. It is the structures a few humans create that push people down."

"What do you mean?" asked John.

"John, if you knew that the person who was making the products you were buying was going hungry because they were not being paid enough, but others who owned the company were getting rich, would you be upset?" asked Phred.

"Of course I would," replied John.

"Well, that is exactly what is happening with many of the things you buy. For example, the jeans you have on were probably made in a sweat shop in Bangladesh. They used to be made in Korea, but the workers there wanted more money so the company moved to Bangladesh where there are so many people hungry that they will work for seventy-five cents a day. Of course you and others in the United States are not even aware of this," explained Phred.

"Phred, you are right I didn't know that, and it is terrible, but what can I do about it?" asked John.

"Like it or not, John, you are part of this system. What can you do about it? Tell others for one. I realize that these incredibly bad power-over structures exist and most people are not aware of them," said Phred.

"Isn't what you are talking about – these "bad power-over structures" – just another way of saying 'capitalism?'" asked John.

"Yes, it is, at least the way capitalism is set up today. But there is something called 'responsible capitalism' where everyone involved receives a fair share of the selling of the products. If humans knew how corporations cut deals to have their products made for the most minimum wage possible, wages that are so bad workers can barely feed their families, in order to make sure the company makes the most profit for themselves and their stockholders, then I truly believe most humans would accept less profit from the selling of a corporation's products in order for everyone to receive a fair living wage," said Phred.

"But wouldn't a company official say 'we would pay more, but if we do then people would invest in our competitors,' because since they pay less to have their product made the other company could offer their shareholders a higher profit?" asked John.

"You got it, John!" replied Phred. "Capitalism as it is used today only cares about the company's bottom line: profit. But responsible capitalism cares about profit and people."

"Phred, I don't really know much about capitalism but isn't responsible capitalism some form of Marxism?" asked John.

"Absolutely not! In Japan some companies have policies that their top executives cannot make more than twenty-five times their lowest-paid employee. In order for an executive to make more money their lowest-paid employee must make more money. And Japan is as capitalistic as we are. But many corporations there follow the practice of responsible capitalism," answered Phred.

"How could something like that happen in America?" asked John.

"Well, again, someone needs to get the word out there that capitalism, the way it is practiced today, causes more people to starve than overpopulation does. But capitalism can be responsible. People just have to decide that they are willing to take a little less so everyone can have a little more. Remember, John, America uses 35% of the world's resources but has only five percent of the world's population."

"And," John said loudly, "materialism doesn't even bring us happiness!"

"Exactly," replied Phred.

"But how do we get corporations to practice responsible capitalism?"

"I wish I could say once the people in the corporation realize that what they are doing is causing people in faraway countries to go hungry then the corporation would voluntarily adopt responsible capitalistic practices, but, unfortunately, I don't believe they will. These executives might want to adopt responsible capitalism practices, but, as you said, they will say they can't because then the company that doesn't will make a higher profit and people will invest in that company and not the one that practices responsible capitalism," said Phred.

"But is that true?" asked John.

"They think it's true, John, but what it really is is just a mental model. There are just as many examples in the world where people will set aside their selfishness for the good of others as there are people being totally selfish."

"So it is possible?" asked John.

"I think it is," said Phred. "But, remember, I'm an optimist. If people in the United States and other first world countries realized that the way they live is hurting others and preventing others from producing small families, I believe they would change."

"Most people already know that materialism is not bringing them happiness," added John.

"That's correct, John, and I'm not saying the people in the United States have to give up all their things. They just need to pay a little more for the things they buy in order for the people that made whatever it is to receive a fair wage."

"Does that already happen in some instances?"

"I think what you might mean is that some products have the Fair Trade label on them," answered Phred.

"Yeah, 'Fair Trade label,' what's that?" asked John.

"The Fair Trade label means that the person making the product is receiving a fair wage for the making of the product. Unfortunately, it has caught on in only a few industries, coffee being the number one industry, but it is growing. The Fair Trade label is very much part of responsible capitalism," explained Phred.

"And are companies that practice Fair Trade making a profit?"

"Absolutely, just not as much profit as a company that pays the people that make the product peanuts."

"But if more and more companies practice Fair Trade then fewer people would go hungry, and if they did not feel poor then they might have fewer children, and we might save the planet."

"Or at least the human race," added Phred. "Because the planet itself is not at risk but the human race is."

"Point taken," replied John. John was quiet for a moment and then added, "Maybe the only way Fair Trade labeling will really take off is by making responsible capitalism a law, or, to be more specific, Fair Trade policies a law?"

"Sounds good to me," said Phred. "In the 1970's the people of your country demanded environmental laws in order to make corporations clean up their messes, so why not laws regarding responsible capitalism and Fair Trade policies? Remember it only takes a small group of people to begin to make a change. America has an environmental vision that says we want to live in an environmentally healthy world, and, even though America needs to do better, you do have cleaner rivers than fifty years ago."

"But we still need to do better, and humans need a new vision for the entire planet," stated John. Again, after a few moments of silence, John said, "What America and the rest of the world need is a new vision. One that supports people to take off all those silly glasses they see life through and create a truly healthy vision for themselves, all Americans, and for the world." With this statement said, Phred nodded in agreement and then closed his eyes as if he needed to rest.

Chapter Seventeen

Several days later, John and Phred took John's fishing boat around Rose Key, hoping the fish were biting on the leeward side of the key.

"Phred, I've been doing a lot of thinking about America needing a new vision. What would this new vision look like?" asked John.

"Well, before we talk about a new vision, tell me what you think is the vision America has now?" asked Phred.

"Hmm… let me think." And, with that, John was quiet for a while. "Well, to start I would say we don't have one. At least not one that is easily defined by everyone. Most people are thinking about food, shelter, clothing, and then what do I want to buy at the mall this week. But I would not call that a vision," answered John.

"Has America ever had a vision of its own?" asked Phred.

"Sure," replied John. "In the beginning of the 20th century our vision had to do with immigration. 'Give us your poor, your hungry, etc.,' and our borders were open to people from all over the world."

"Good, John, and later in the century I remember one of your leaders saying his vision for America was a car in every garage and a chicken in every pot. And, for many, both these visions have come to pass. But what about today?" asked Phred.

"I cannot think of any. Maybe at the individual level the vision is to get an education in order to get a good job. But what is a 'good job?' Most people would probably say one that pays well. Again, so they can go to the mall." With that said, John was quiet again.

The sea is a great place to think. Especially on a beautiful sunny day with calm seas. Again, after a prolonged silence, John said, "America does not have a clear vision, but we do have a few that might be trying to emerge. Like, we realize that our dependency upon other nations for energy hurts us, so the vision of being energy free from other nations is emerging. And we know this energy needs to be clean energy, such as solar or wind. With global climate change finally being accepted as something that is not only happening but which also is not a good thing, I think an environmental vision might be emerging."

"I like where you are going, John. A vision needs to offer people a better place to work towards than where they are going now. Global climate change, pollution, the awareness that buying things does not bring us happiness, etc. America might be ready for a new vision around environmental thinking."

"A Green Vision, Phred!" exclaimed John.

"Okay, John, what would a green vision look like?" responded Phred.

"Well, for one, we would have to be energy clean. This means that our energy will have to come from places that do not cause pollution. Solar or wind power would be good," said John.

"Good, what else would your vision have?" asked Phred.

"People would turn away from buying things all the time as a way of trying to be happy," said John.

"But where would they turn to?" asked Phred.

John thought for a moment. "True happiness comes to you when your true self finds its purpose in life." After another silence he continued, "And your true purpose in life is about being part of something greater than yourself that makes the world a better place for more than just you."

"Again, good," said Phred. "And how will they do that?"

"First, people have to realize that the different colored glasses they were taught to wear gave them some unhealthy mental models and take the glasses off," answered John.

"Okay, let's say people realize that they are wearing colored glasses that create unhealthy mental models, and, in their minds, they take the glasses off. What do they see now?" asked Phred, happy John was thinking about this.

"Well, now that they have taken off the glasses and realize that material things, power over others, always looking for the good times, etc., does not lead to real happiness, but also, in abundance, hurts others and the planet, each person will need to discover what their true self and purpose in life is, since happiness comes from this," answered John.

"And how do they do this?"

"For one, people also need to realize that you don't wake up one day and think, 'Hey I now know my true self and purpose in life.' It's not that simple or easy. Discovering your true self and purpose is a *journey of exploring and learning* about who you are, understanding what mental models you have that are healthy and unhealthy, then changing the unhealthy ones, and finally, but maybe most important, 'how you are connected to all living things.' said John. With this said, John was quiet while he pondered what he had just said. After about a minute of silence he continued, "Phred, the road the human race is going down is the wrong one, and we have to learn to think and live differently. Seeing the importance of exploring and learning, and how we are connected to all living things, can lead to healthy mental models, but this kind of learning, and putting this learning into action, will take time. Of course, one good thing about humans is that learning is something they have the ability to do."

"You mean humans need to go to school more?" asked Phred with a mischievous smile.

"No, going to school is only one way we learn. And most schools are teaching us to continue down this wrong road anyway. Phred, we need to explore new ways of living and learn from it."

"I agree," replied Phred. "Let's hear the answer for you, John. As of today, who are you? What is your purpose in life? What mental models do you have that are healthy, and which ones are unhealthy that need to be changed? And how are you connected to other living things?"

"Okay, for me: Who is my true self? Well, I know one of the places I am most happy is when I am on the water. I feel more connected to nature out here. I am the son of John and Mary Russell and they are doing their best to raise me to be the person I choose to become. I also know I am the friend of Phred whose friendship means a lot to me!"

"Okay, now tell me, what do all those things have in common?" asked Phred.

"I don't know. They are all about me?" answered John.

"Yeah, and what else?"

John thought for a moment and then said, "I don't know."

"They are all about you in connection with something or someone else! Your connection with nature, your parents, me, etc., and, John, your true purpose is not just about who you are connected to but also how you are connected, and these relationships create a greater whole." said Phred.

"Huh? You are losing me," replied John.

"John, remember, finding your true purpose and being happy is partly based on being connected to something greater than yourself."

"Okay, I know that."

"This is because your true purpose and happiness come from the relationships you create and from what you learn and do with these relationships. In other words, the relationships are the link to the greater whole. Or, to put it more bluntly:

> *'Life is all about the relationships you create with the*
> *world, and what you learn and do with these relationships'.*

"Wow, Phred, something else I need to think about," answered John.

"Let me give you an example. When you think of your parents what do you think of?"

"Two great adults who love me very much," answered John.

"Good. What is the connection/relationship between you and them?"

"Well, love of course."

"Again, good. What is your connection/relationship with, say, your bicycle?" asked Phred.

"I love riding it."

"What about with your bicycle mechanic?"

"Good guy, and keeps my bicycle working well," said John. "But, Phred, what are you getting at?"

"What I'm trying to say is your connection/relationship to your bicycle and your mechanic is just as important as the bicycle itself. Just as your connection/relationship to your parents, or 'love,' is just as important as your parents themselves. Understand this, feel this, and you will have begun to change one of humans' truly unhealthy mental models to a healthy one."

"And that is?"

"Right now the mental model is 'my parents are important,' or 'my bicycle is important.' The new mental model is 'my connection/relationship with my parents (love) is equally as important as my parents themselves, and my connection/relationship to my bicycle (including the person who maintains it) is just as important as the bicycle itself and riding it.'" At present humans pay attention to the objects or the people that are important to them, but if they gave equal importance to their relationships to these objects or people, then humans would not be so unconsciously destructive towards the planet."

"Why?" asked John.

"Because by paying attention, or being mindful, to the relationships, people will begin to understand the importance of their relationships with all living and non-living things."

"I know what you mean, Phred. My dad really enjoys his car, but he also appreciates his mechanic and the friendship they have formed over caring for his car."

"Good example, John. Your dad also doesn't buy a new car every few years, but takes care of the one he has, which lasts a long time. I also know he even feels slightly guilty because it is a gasoline-driven engine, and I heard him say his next car will be an electric one."

"And I'm sure my Dad will take care of this next car too versus trading it in every few years for a new one. But, Phred, do you really think humans can learn to live in a way where they appreciate the relationships they have more than their things?"

"Sure, John, why not? They have in the past. Back when the human occupation was primarily farming or hunting, people were very much in tune with their relationships. And I am even beginning to see it more in today's society with 'buy local' campaigns, or 'Fair Trade Labels.' You humans have the incredible ability to change and grow when you want to."

John pondered for a moment and said, "In buy local campaigns people know they are supporting their local farms and merchants, so the connection/relationship can be at two levels. One, people know they are supporting their neighbors, who they might not know personally, but they can still feel a geography connection with them. Or two, it is very possible they do know their neighbor because, for instance, their neighbor runs a small store where they shop, so they've developed a personal relationship." John stopped for a moment and then continued, "As for the Fair Trade Label, people know that their money is going towards paying someone who produced the product a livable wage, and hence they feel the connection. Yeah, maybe people can change. And, since people have to pay a little more for these connections, they know they are making a statement that these relationships are important to them."

John could tell the sun was beginning to go down out over the bay, so, with much to think about, John and Phred headed for home.

The next day while walking along the beach, John said to Phred, "Phred, let me see if I can answer the question about relationships for me."

"Okay," said Phred.

"For me," Phred could see John seriously thinking, "happiness is when I am out here fishing with you, Phred, because I have a connection/relationship with you and nature."

"I agree, but tell me more about this connection/relationship. What do you learn from it?" asked Phred.

John paused to think. "I learn that when I am outside in nature, spending time with my best friend, fishing, and talking that life feels good. I also enjoy having these talks because I learn from them."

"Good," said Phred, "so now you know three things about your true purpose in life and what makes you happy:

> *(1) You enjoy having a connection/relationship with the outdoors*
> *(2) You enjoy connecting to another living thing - me*
> *(3) You enjoy learning."*

"Yeah, that is an excellent way of saying what makes me happy," answered John.

"Well, those three things are very much in line with what you were doing as a baby. Learning, connecting with other living things, and enjoying the environment around you. If others could take the time to rediscover that these things are elements of their true purpose and what truly makes us happy, we might be able to save the planet for you humans," said Phred.

"And how would knowing these three things save the planet?" asked John.

"If people took off all the different colored glasses they wear and understood that life is about learning, relationships with other living things, and enjoying the environment around them – again relationships – then they would be willing to change the way they live by taking more time to learn, and grow and recognize all the relationships they have in order to live happier and fuller lives," said Phred.

"And we could turn away from this destructive path we are on as a species and save the planet," exclaimed John.

"Exactly. Now, knowing this, describe your idea of a green vision," said Phred.

"Well, first we still need renewable energy, but along with renewable energy we need to learn to live differently with each other. Let's see, instead of suburban neighborhoods where we all live separately, how about energy-efficient apartments with lots of common outdoor and indoor space in order to strengthen our relationships with others and the environment around us. And, since we need to learn how to live differently, we first need to learn how to create dialogue between us so we can learn together."

"It sounds like you are creating a commune, like human beings had in the 1960s?" said Phred.

John pondered this and then said, "No, I know I may sound like I'm creating a commune, but they didn't work. I remember my dad once talking about them and saying there was all this pressure to conform to the commune's rules. They may have preached free love but in the end many of them were as strict with their rules as mainstream society was and still is. What I'm talking about are new communication methods that create dialogue in order for power-with and power-from-within to flourish. Remember, Phred, you said in dialogue people spend time trying to understand each other's ideas, values, mental models, and beliefs." Again John stopped to gather his thoughts. "And since the idea is to create something new, people in dialogue for a green vision will need to examine their own thoughts, ideas, mental models, and values. Even after removing all the glasses, we will need to explore and learn about where do we want the human race to go."

After another moment of silence John continued, "But, Phred, I understand now that life is:

(1) About learning – not like school learning where it is all about memorizing facts, but dialogue learning where you truly try to understand yourself, others, and the world.

(2) About relationships with other living things – not the superficial relationship we have now where our material things are more important than the people who make these material things.

(3) And, finally, about enjoying the environment around us, which is, again, part of the process of relationships."

When John finished he looked up at Phred and said, "You know, I think I get it now!"

"Yeah, John, I think you do. Now go out and teach others," said Phred as they pulled up to John's dock while the last spark of light from the sun could be seen on the horizon.

PART THREE

A NEW ROAD
(Ten years later)

Chapter Eighteen

John walked into his studio apartment and yelled, "Phred, I'm home." Phred, who had been sunning himself on the windowsill answered, "Welcome home, old friend, how was your day?"

While hanging his bicycle on the wall rack, John said, "Excellent! We received a new shipment of green light bulbs at the hardware store, and, with so many people buying only green light bulbs, they are now cheaper than the old, filament, high-energy-consumption light bulbs. But the best part of my day was, after getting off from work at 1:00 P.M., I rode my bike through the park and spent the afternoon at the adult learning drop-in center having Mr. Clemens read over my story."

Phred was older, but, except for a few gray whiskers, he looked the same. "Sounds like a good day, John. I have been enjoying the sun and the sea breeze coming off the ocean. When are we going to go fishing again?"

"Don't worry, we will get out this weekend. My dad wants us to stop by the hotel and help him fix one of those new water-saving shower devices he had put in five years ago. After helping him, we can take the skiff out to Sunset Key and fish," replied John. "Do you want to hear what Mr. Clemens said?"

"Sure," said Phred.

"Well, he agreed with us that that our society is fundamentally flawed. As long as the human race has the mental model 'in order to survive we must control our environment,' we are going down the tubes environmentally. The human race must move to a new mental model along the lines of 'in order to survive we must learn to live together with all living things.'"

"Has the human race ever done this?" asked Phred.

John thought for a moment and then said, "Maybe before humans learned how to grow their own food they lived more in harmony with nature."

"So you and Mr. Clemens think that humans must go back to being hunters and gatherers?"

"No, of course not, we are not going to go back, but we need to go forward and evolve."

"Evolve to what?" asked Phred.

"That's the million dollar question, my friend. Phred, you're the one that has for years now been pushing me to create my own new vision for the human race, and I've told you some of my ideas of ways humans are evolving slowly, but we both know evolution is not something that happens quickly. Evolution is usually a slow process of many people adopting new ideas and ways of living. But, as you and I know, we are on the road."

"True," said Phred. "Tell me more about what you and Mr. Clemens talked about."

"Well, he also liked my idea about how part of our evolution is for all of us to move away from all the unhealthy, power-over structures which dominate our culture, and move towards more partnership structures. What he wanted to see were examples of partnerships."

"Well, have you written yet about the partnership you created at the hardware store?" asked Phred.

"Not yet, but I did explain it to Mr. Clemens."

"Good, tell me how you described it to him."

"Okay, I said that when Mr. Perkins came to me and offered me the weekend manager's position I said I would take it if I could manage it the way I wanted. Mr. Perkins agreed to this, so I had a meeting with the four other people that worked weekends and explained that, as the weekend manager, I wanted us to create a partnership group in how we worked together. As I said to Mr. Clemens, at first the staff were suspicious of me, thinking I just wanted to somehow get more work out of them and do less myself, but then they were very surprised when I told them that I would take the increase in salary I was receiving for being manager and share some of it among the five of us! That got their attention! Ultimately, I am still the one responsible for what goes on in the store on weekends so I am paid a little more than the others, but, since I wanted to show how partnership will benefit all of us, I gave everyone a share of my increase in salary. We were then able to work together to figure out who did what shift and how we would cover for each other when necessary. This has worked so well that customers have even made comments to Mr. Perkins about how well the store runs on weekends, when he is not around. Several customers have even commented on the positive atmosphere in the store on the weekends. They said it actually looks like his employees are enjoying themselves. And you know what, Phred? We are!"

"But, John, as I have said before, what you are describing is not capitalism," exclaimed Phred.

"Sure it is, Phred. The store still exists to make money. I'm just using partnership to create community among the staff, and that also stretches to include the customers. Besides, according to Mr. Perkins, sales are up over the weekends. He thinks customers that usually waited to go to the big box hardware stores on the weekend are now coming to us.

"And, well," John continued, "if partnership can increase sales than it has possibilities in America and elsewhere. Anyway, I would like to talk more, but tonight I'm on clean-up in the Coop kitchen so I need to go."

Chapter Nineteen

John rented his studio apartment in the town's cohousing apartment complex. Cohousing apartment complexes had been on the rise all over America for the past ten years. They are usually made up of apartments that have only one or two rooms and a bathroom. The kitchen is communal. Residents of John's cohousing complex ate their evening meal together and kept the kitchen stocked with basic foods so people could make themselves breakfast or lunch when they wanted. One of the best parts about the kitchen set-up was, since the residents bought their food in bulk, John's and everyone else's food budgets were much less than they would have been if they were living alone with a kitchen in each apartment. Another benefit was that there was always healthy food like fruits and vegetables around. Before John moved into the cohousing he gravitated towards fast food. Now he ate and felt much better.

John left his room and wandered down to the communal eating area. On his way he passed the 'rec room' where several of his friends were battling it out over a computer game on the big screen TV. Other days John would join them, but today he wanted to make sure none of the recycling bins were full. The cohousing community was proud of their sign in the kitchen that said, 'We recycle ninety-nine percent of what we use in this kitchen.' John and several others were working towards making the recycling one hundred percent.

"Hi John," said Mike, his neighbor, as John sat down at one of the dining room tables. "Did you catch today's economic indicators on CNN?"

"No, I was at the Adult Learning Center all afternoon," replied John.

"Well, according to the government, the NQL indicator is up five percent over last year, while the GNP has leveled off for the third year in a row."

Mary, who had also just sat down, asked, "What is the NQL again?"

Mike replied, "The NQL, or National Quality of Life indicator, started to become popular about ten to fifteen years ago. Some college professors created it because they felt the GNP, or Growth National Product, was way too limited in trying to gauge the growth of our country."

John politely interrupted and added, "Not only is the GNP limited, but in many ways it also can hurt us when we think of the growth of our country only in terms of economic or material growth."

"True," said Mike. "So the NQL tries to measure a more holistic way of looking at our lives and how we are doing. For instance, the NQL measures the healthiness of our overall human environment with nature. We are, as a country, beginning to take better care of all the natural resources we have."

"The NQL also measures how many Americans say they are living happy and meaningful lives," interjected John. "Remember, it wasn't that long ago that most Americans measured their happiness solely based on how many things they could buy."

"Oh, there are still many people doing that," replied Mary.

"Also true," said Mike, "but this is changing more quickly than ever. As people change how they see the world, in this case going from seeing growth in strictly economic terms to seeing growth more holistically or, to use the now popular phrase, in terms of 'green growth and living,' more and more people will buy into the NQL."

"Look how many cohousing places are sprouting up all around us," said John. "There was a time when people felt that they had to have their own home and be an island unto themselves with their families in order to consider themselves successful. Not only was that incredibly inefficient energy-wise, utilizing way more natural resources than we do here living together, but it was also incredibly lonely for many."

"Yeah, there was a time when I didn't really know my neighbors except to wave to them as they drove by in their cars," said Mary.

"And many of those neighbors spent more time in front of their TVs than talking to others. That old book called Bowling Alone really said it all," added Mike. "People really did isolate themselves in their suburban homes. It might have been fine while the kids were growing up and the parents were all wrapped up in their kids' activities, but after the kids left the parents realized they were so wrapped up in their jobs and kids they didn't have any real friends."

"This is why more and more retired people are joining us in co-housing. They want to be around others and yet still retire to their own rooms for peace and quiet," said John.

"And they're great to have around," said Mary. "Did you know Mr. Thomson fixed my leaky faucet yesterday while I was at work? And when I offered to pay him he wouldn't let me."

"Mary, you made Mr. Thomson feel useful. That is more than enough," said John.

"He was useful!" replied Mary. "So is Katherine Wilson, who wakes up every morning before any of us to get down to start the coffee."

"Yeah, Ms. Wilson told me she has been waking up early for the past forty years and that's not going to change. Having the seniors around is a major benefit to all of us," said Mike.

John got up out of his seat and said, "Who would like another cup of Katherine's excellent coffee?" Mary answered, "Yes, please," and John went off to the kitchen to refill his cup and Mary's.

Chapter Twenty

When John returned Mary said, "Thank you," as she took a sip, and then she continued, "Let's go back to this NQL. How do they measure 'living happy and meaningful lives?'"

"Ah, good question," said John. "In order to measure something like that, we need to first define what it means to be 'living happy and meaningful lives?'" John stopped for a moment to think. He hadn't talked to many people over the years about what he had learned from Phred, so talking about it now made him a little nervous. "Many years ago an old friend once told me that the journey *to living a happy and meaningful life requires discovering your true purpose in life and then following it.*"

"What?" said Mike.

"Well the exact words were: '*The key to happiness is discovering your true purpose in life and then following it.*'"

"And how do I find my true purpose in life?" asked Mary.

John could tell she was enjoying the conversation. In some ways John was beginning to understand how Phred must have felt so many years ago when he explained these ideas to John. "Well, *discovering your true purpose in life is a dance between trying new things, gaining a better understanding of who you are, and developing a deeper understanding of the world around you.*"

"I like to dance," said Mary.

"I don't," said Mike.

"I don't actually mean dance," replied John. "By using the word 'dance' I am trying to convey that discovering your true purpose in life is not something that happens all at once. In other words, you do not wake up one day and say, 'Hey, I now know what my true purpose in life is.'"

"All right, I get it doesn't happen instantaneously, but how about over, say, a week or two?" asked Mary.

"It's a little more complicated than that. By dance I'm also trying to move away from our western, linear way of thinking to a more circular way of thinking." John paused for a moment and then continued, "Most of us were taught to think in linear steps, like one, two, three, etc., until we have the answer. Discovering your true purpose does not work like that," said John.

"Then how does it work?" inquired Mike.

"As I said, there *are three components: trying new things, understanding yourself better, and developing a deeper understanding of the world around you.* And you do these three things all at the same time, following a circular process of *action-mindfulness observation-reflection-action,*" said John.

"What?" exclaimed Mike.

John smiled and said, "I hear you, Mike. It sounds weird, but it really isn't." John knew Mike liked John. They had worked together on several cohousing projects and had bonded over being very task-oriented yet with a belief that any kind of work should also be fun.

"So, break it down for me, and remember I'm not that smart," said Mike.

"Okay, let's first take 'action,' or trying new things. Unlike what our high school teachers liked to tell us, most of us do not figure out what we want to do in life by reading books. Oh, sure, reading can give us insights about the world, but we don't really know if we like something until we actually do it. Most of us learn best by doing, and we don't know if we like something or not until we actually do it! Consequently, taking action by trying new things is crucial to discovering your true purpose in life," said John.

"But John, you cannot become a doctor and then decide you don't like it so you become a lawyer. It is just not practical," replied Mary.

"No, of course not, Mary, but you can volunteer in a hospital to see what being in that kind of setting is like. You might find out you like helping people, or you may discover that dealing with sick people is not to your liking. Two good things to know about yourself before you go off to medical school. But I'm not just talking about finding a profession or job that suits you. Discovering your true purpose is much more than just finding a job that you like. Trying new things means go on a hike, bike ride across your state, volunteer in a soup kitchen, do an internship in a company you think you might want to work for someday, travel and see how other people live, go to a music festival, stop and help out a stranger, but keep pushing yourself out of your comfort zone at least once a day. In other words, try new things. And, for the record, this is in fact *the first principle of discovering your true purpose in life: trying new things, gaining a better understanding of who you are, and developing a deeper understanding of the world around you through a circular process of action-mindfulness observation-reflection-action,*" said John.

"What do you mean by 'mindfulness observation?'" asked Mary.

John seemed to have everyone's attention, so he continued, "What I mean by observation is we learn to watch what we are thinking as we go through our day and we try to discover what our mental models are."

"Oh, we have talked about this before," said Mary. "For instance, my mental model until recently was that in order to be a good parent I needed to own my own house, and that's just not true."

"But many people think that," Mike butted in.

"Can someone please tell me what a mental model is?" asked Dory who had just recently come in the room and joined them.

Mike, John, and Mary all looked at each other. Finally, Mary replied, "Sorry, Dory, mental models are something the three of us have talked about before. Let's see if I can explain, though it was John that first described them. *Mental models are unconscious assumptions or rules society teaches us about how the world works which we then act out in our daily lives. The second principle of discovering your true purpose is understanding your mental models and changing the unhealthy ones.*"

"Huh?" said Dory.

"Let me give you an example. Since John first told me about mental models I have been doing a lot of thinking about them. What is your assumption when you hear someone is a straight-'A' student?"

Dory thought for a minute and then said, "That they are smart."

"Okay, what is your assumption about a student that receives all 'D's?"

"That they are stupid," replied Dory.

"Why do you think that way?" asked Mary.

"Huh?" said Dory. "Because they are."

"Do you know Frank at the service station in the middle of town?"

"Yeah, I know Frank. He's a great auto mechanic!" Dory said, wondering where this conversation was going.

"That's him, and I agree the guy is a great mechanic with electric cars and also with all the old, polluting, gasoline-powered cars. Well, in high school Frank was a 'D' student. Do you think he is stupid?" asked Mary.

"I see where you are going, Mary. Yes, I do think Frank is smart. Maybe he wasn't book smart but he sure knows cars."

"Good, but he is also an avid reader. Last time I was in his shop he was reading Ulysses."

"Oh right, maybe 'book smart' is not the right phrase. But you know what I mean," said Dory.

"Yes, I know exactly what you mean, and now we get back to the concept of mental models. *Mental models are unconscious assumptions or rules society teaches us about how the world works which we then act out in our daily lives.* In the case of what society considers smart, we are taught that getting 'A's is smart and getting 'D's is stupid, and most people buy into these ideas and then act out their lives accordingly. But these ideas are not facts, they are just mental models society has taught us to believe unconsciously," said Mary.

"I am beginning to see where you are going. Society teaches us things that we believe are facts and yet they are not," said Dory.

"Correct, and what makes it particularly bad is if you think these ideas are 'facts of life' and you are one of the people in the world who gets 'D's you will think that you are stupid and cannot learn anything and then play this out by not trying to learn. Like, 'why should I learn anything? I'm stupid,'" said Mary.

"But Frank does not think he is stupid!"

"True, but I'm afraid he is one of the exceptions," Mary replied. "I once asked him how he got into learning about cars and books. His answer was that even though he never did well in school his dad always encouraged him to tinker with things and also to read. Not school books, though Frank did try to read the books his teacher assigned, but also any book he found interesting. I then asked him if he thought he was smart. He said he used to think he was stupid because he never did well on school tests even though he studied a lot. He just could not remember the answers to the test questions. But once he finished high school, with more encouragement from his father, he began working on cars and discovered he was really good at fixing them. In the end he decided he was smart at some things. So to answer your question, yes, Frank does think he is smart.

"Which illustrates my point," Mary continued. "Getting straight 'D's does not mean you are stupid, nor does getting straight 'A's automatically mean you are smart at all things. Chances are students getting 'A's are just good at memorizing answers to the test questions. Again, this is an example of mental models."

"Okay, how do mental models tie into discovering your true purpose in life and being happy?" asked Dory.

"Remember, the second principle for discovering your true purpose in life is understanding our mental models and changing the unhealthy ones," said John.

"Because there are many mental models about what is supposed to make us happy that are just not true and are unhealthy for us," interrupted Mary. "For instance, I believed that in order to be a good parent I needed to own a home in suburbia. Society teaches us that good parents own their own homes. But I discovered while trying to obtain this dream that I had to work all the time in order to save enough money to make this dream come true and, consequently, I did not spend that much time with my children."

"What Mary is talking about is called 'chasing the dime' and is very common in our society. People believe owning your own home or making a lot of money brings people security," inserted Mike. *"The third principle for discovering your true purpose in life is recognizing there isn't any security in life, outside the security of knowing, who you are, being that person to the best of your ability, and continuing growing and learning your entire life."*

"Yes, that is what I was doing! Always chasing the dime. And it was unhealthy for my kids and me. I never really spent any quality time with them, and I was always stressed that we did not have enough money," said Mary.

When Mary stopped talking John added, "Mary, did you have many friends in the neighborhood?"

"Not really," replied Mary. "Oh sure, I knew my neighbors to wave to as I ran from work to one kid's activity to another, but I never really spent any time with them. Not like here. Suburbia isn't really set up for connecting with each other." Mary took a moment to pause and then continued, "Many things were wrong with my life because

I accepted the mental model 'good parents own their own home' as a fact of life and then tried to live up to it. You see, Dory, not all mental models are bad, but *the second principle of discovering your true purpose in life is to first be aware of what your mental models are and how you are acting out your life because of them. Second, decide if your mental models are healthy or unhealthy, and, third, change the ones that are unhealthy to healthy ones and act out your life accordingly.*"

"And how do we do that?" asked Dory.

"You start by being mindful and observing how you think," answered John. "In other words, take a moment, watch your thinking and say to yourself, 'Why do I think this way? What are the mental models behind why I think this way, and how do I act out these mental models in my day-to-day living?" John paused for a moment and then continued, "Training yourself to do this is not easy. Here in the west we are not trained in being mindful."

"Being mindful?" said Dory.

"*The fourth principle in discovering your true purpose is practicing mindfulness observation. Being aware of the present moment slows down your thinking, helps you appreciate your life at that moment, and helps you observe your own thinking and discover your mental models.* Then the mental models that are healthy we keep, but the ones that are not we find healthier ones and then try to live according to them," said John.

Chapter Twenty-One

At that moment Mary's twin eight-year-old children came running into the room. "Hi Mom, we are home," they shouted.

"Hi guys," said Mary. "How was school?"

"Great," said Giles, Mary's boy. Erica, Mary's girl, pulled out her notebook and showed her Mom the drawing she had done that day. It was a drawing of people in Africa. At the bottom of the page were a few math problems. "Oh Mom, we learned about Africa today," Giles continued. "Did you know that families in Africa are larger than families in America? See, Erica figured it out," and Giles pointed to the bottom of Erica's drawing.

"Nice work, Erica! You can tell me more about it at dinner. Why don't you two go back to our apartment and clean up before dinner?"

"Okay, Mom. Come on, Giles," said Erica, and both children dashed towards the staircase that led to their apartment.

Once they were gone John said, "Wow, they sure look a lot happier coming home from school than I was at that age."

"Oh, they are," replied Mary. "They're much happier than all of us. Ever since the public schools finally adopted the 'teaching how to learn' programs and policies, children have been learning the natural way."

"Man, these are interesting conversations. Okay, I'll bite," said Mike, "What is learning the natural way?"

Mary took a moment and then began, "Children, like humans of all ages, really, are naturally inquisitive. They want to learn from the moment they enter this world. Our job and their teachers' job is to feed this natural inquisitiveness by showing them ways of learning that increase this natural desire to learn."

"All I did in school was memorize stuff and then take tests to show I memorized it. Of course, two seconds after the test I forgot ninety-nine percent of what I learned, and I did not come home as happy as your children just did," said Mike.

"None of us did, Mike. Memorizing information is not a natural way we learn," said John.

"There is nothing interesting about being told you need to memorize this information," added Mary.

"Then what is this other way your kids are being taught?" asked Mike again.

"Teaching how to learn is exactly that," said Mary. "My kids are being taught how to discover knowledge the same way they have since they came into the world: by asking themselves questions and learning how to answer them themselves."

John interjected, "Thanks to computers there is so much knowledge available to us today that memorizing seems obsolete. Today, children need to learn two skills: one, how to access knowledge, and, two, to fine-tune and enhance their natural desire to learn by asking themselves questions and discovering the answers. Which actually brings us to the fifth principle. One of the great educators of our times said:

> *People will learn:*
> *- 20% of what they hear*
> *- 40% of what they hear and see*
> *- 80% of what they discover for themselves.*

"Who said that?" asked Mike.

"I believe it was Mark Twain, and I think he was quoting Socrates, but an educator named Dr. Jane Vella writes quite a bit about it," answered John. He then continued, "The second skill is a much harder skill to teach than the first. Teachers that can truly inspire their students to want to learn are unfortunately not in the majority."

"True," said Mary, "but that is changing. My kids' teacher is young, and it's clear to me that her training to be a teacher was very different than the older teachers."

"I'm still trying to get my arms around this whole new way of teaching," said Mike. "I kind-of get the idea of teaching children how to learn versus having them memorize information, but, for example, I had to memorize all the countries in, say, South America, and their capitals, and I turned out okay."

"Today, " said Mary, "my kids don't memorize the countries and capitals, but in groups students pick a country and research who the people are, what the country looks like, and they are told to find out something about the country that would make them want to visit it someday. Then they put on a show for the class to demonstrate what they learned. This way they learn to have a better understanding and appreciation of other cultures."

"Okay, but in high school when kids are preparing to apply for college how do you prove they are learning the material that they will need to know once they are in college?" asked Mike.

"What do you think colleges believe students need to know?" replied John.

"Oh, I don't know. I guess English, algebra, biology, some history," said Mike.

"In your opinion, why do they need to know this kind of knowledge?"

"I don't know. Maybe English so they learn to write well, algebra in order to balance their checkbook or figure out how long it will take to them to travel to where they are going, biology so they will understand how their body works and something about the world around them, and history so they know what has happened in the past," answered Mike.

"Cool," said John. "Now, what do all your answers have in common?"

"I don't know, do you?"

"Here is what I think they have in common: they all are relevant to something students will use in their lives," replied John.

"Okay, so what?"

"Well along with many educators believing that people learn eighty percent of what they discover for themselves, many of them also believe that people learn best when what they are learning is useful to them. *The complete fifth principle for discovering your true purpose is that people learn eighty percent of what they discover for themselves and learn best when what they are learning is useful to them.* So, in high school and college courses that are taught by having students work on problem-solving projects that students see as useful the student will truly learn," said John.

"I can give you an example of what John is talking about with a current school project my kids have been working on concerning them learning about cancer," said Mary. Everyone turned to give

Mary their attention. "Unfortunately, today everyone knows someone who has had or has cancer. Did you know that our government did not even keep statistics on cancer until 1927? It's true. Cancer is a major killer today but it wasn't one hundred years ago."

"Why is that, I wonder," asked Mike.

"Well, we have learned that eighty to ninety percent of all cancers are from exposure to environmental factors," John offered. "The bottom line is cancer-causing substances have increased greatly in the last century and into this one. These cancer-causing substances have increased so much that cancer is now the number-one killer of our species."

"That stinks," interjected Mike.

"True, and we are at least beginning to try to change that, but now I want to get back to teaching biology. How to clean up our world of cancer-causing materials is another conversation, but I will say that knowing biology helps us increase our efforts to clean up our world," John continued.

"How so?" asked Mike.

"Because biology classes today are taught by asking students to answer two questions: one, how is cancer affecting our bodies, and, two, where are cancer-causing substances coming from? And what do you think high school students have to learn in order for them to answer these questions themselves?" asked John.

"Let's see," said Mike. After a moment he continued, "They would have to understand what cells are, and also cell division. Then, after that, they would have to understand how our bodies are made up of organs and organs are made up of cells... But, you know, they might already know the organs of the body, because I remember my brother telling me about how his son, who is in second grade, made models of the human body out of typical classroom materials: rubber bands, scrap paper, etc. They did not learn about cells, so, in high school, students will have to learn how organs are made up of cells," said Mike.

"Good, and how do you think they should learn about cells and cell division?" asked John.

"I know for John the answer is not 'lecture about cells and then give them a test,'" said Mary.

There was a pause, so John continued, "Okay, I loved how Mike's nephew learned about the organs in our bodies by building a model of our bodies using classroom scraps. Why can't high school students learn the same way?"

"High school kids are not going to want to play with scraps of paper and rubber bands, John," said Mike.

"How about having them use PowerPoint? They could make a PowerPoint showing a cell in detail and then they could even show cell division. It is amazing what young people can do with a computer," said John.

"They could even show a cancer-causing substance attacking a normal cell and creating a cancer cell," said Mary, becoming excited about the possibilities of learning this way. "The project my kids are doing in class only had them investigating questions about cancer. Learning about cells this way the students are doing exactly what you said, John, they are learning it by discovering and presenting for themselves how cancer works, about cells, and about cell division. And," now Mary was becoming even more excited, "the chances of the students remembering this knowledge is much greater because people learn eighty percent of what they discover for themselves!"

Everyone was silent for a moment enjoying Mary's excitement over the conversation. Finally Mike added, "I agree the chances of them remembering this knowledge are much greater. We know if they had to memorize the knowledge they would forget most of it as soon as the test was over. But I see another advantage for teaching this way. By having them discover the knowledge for themselves they will learn the process of how to discover other knowledge."

"I agree, Mike, but I do see one problem with this process," said Mary. "Students will also have to learn what on the Internet is considered valid knowledge and what is just crap, because anyone can put anything on the Internet. But I already know the answer to this problem. Teachers will have to create another exercise showing their students how to evaluate websites."

"You all understand how teaching and learning is changing for the better," said John. "Now, how are the students going to answer the second question about where the cancer-causing substances are coming from?"

"Okay, they would have to research this too on the Internet," said Mike. "But this is an example of where teachers are going to have to really stress the need to evaluate where they are finding the information from."

"I agree," said John. "And once they discover which substances cause cancer, they are then going to have to discover where in our environment are we putting these substances."

"Right," replied Mary, "but by doing that aren't they now getting a lesson in environmental science? I thought this was a biology class," said Mary.

"It is a biology class, but should the teacher not teach an environmental science lesson?" asked John.

"Well, no, of course answering the question about where cancer-causing substances come from is important but I was just saying this is a biology class," Mary said again.

"So, right now, or at least when we were all in high school, teaching science was broken down into specific disciplines: biology, physics, chemistry, and I don't even think we had environmental science. But what is essentially wrong with breaking up all this knowledge and teaching them separately?"

John paused and then continued, "What's wrong is life doesn't work like that. *The six principle of discovering your true purpose in life is to understand that everything is interconnected,* and yet all we see are pieces because that is how we were taught to learn," stated John. "I learned as a young boy that schools were teaching me to memorize information in science classes, events in history or social studies, figures and formulas in math classes, and spelling and grammar in English classes, but *no one tried to teach me – or, more appropriately, helped me learn – why all this was important. And absolutely no one tried to help me try to discover how it is all interconnected.*"

"Wait a second," said Mike, "My teachers told me I would need all this knowledge to get a good job someday, and they were right. I have a good job."

"Okay, Mike, do you love your job?" asked John.

"Love my job?" Mike said, as if this were an absurd question. "Well, no, but who does?"

"I do," replied John. "I truly do."

"John, you work in a hardware store," said Mary. "Don't get me wrong, being a hardware salesman is great, but how can you love what you do?"

"Two reasons. One, I like helping people, and, two, I know I am serving a purpose. It may be a small purpose, granted, but I know I am helping the customer solve a problem that somehow makes their life better. In other words, *I see the big picture of how my little job is interconnected to everything else.*" John made this last statement with the centeredness of a man who is truly happy and there was silence around the table.

Finally Mary said, "John, you said earlier that '*The key to happiness is discovering your true purpose in life and then following it.*' Does this mean you have found your true purpose?"

"Good question, Mary. I think I have, though *the seventh principle in discovering your true purpose is that it's a lifelong process and sometimes it evolves or changes over time.* So, though I have found my true purpose for now, still it might change in time."

Chapter Twenty-Two

Mary paused for a moment and then said, "John, you have obviously been thinking about how to discover your true purpose for a while now. Are you saying that discovering your true purpose in life and then following it is a lifelong process?"

Mike interrupted and said, "You mean I'm not going to know until the end of my life why I am here?"

"Possibly, Mike, but two things," said John. "One, chances are you will figure a lot of it out once you start thinking about it, especially by using the process of action-mindfulness observation-reflection-action, and, two, it may take your whole life to figure it out and then follow it, but so far, from my experience, the journey has been totally worth it."

"But can you tell us what your true purpose is as of today?" asked Mary.

"I can try," replied John. *"What I have discovered over time, by observing, trying and reflecting on new things, changing my unhealthy mental models, deepening my understanding of how the world works, and talking and connecting with others, is that my true purpose in life is to support ways that help the human race learn to live more sustainably."*

"Wow," said Mary. "But how is being a hardware salesman helping you do that, and did you really figure this out all on your own?"

"Those are two very different questions, Mary, but let me try and answer them. First, did I really figure this out all on my own? Well, when it comes to finding my true purpose I did answer this question by myself, but I had help from a mentor in understanding the process of why and how I needed to learn my true purpose." In

John's mind he said, Thank you Phred. "To answer the second question, as a hardware salesman I am always asking my customers if they are interested in green technology, but what's even more satisfying is that I have been able to introduce a structure of partnership among the weekend staff."

"Why is partnership important? Though I admit it sounds cool," asked Mike.

"Because it is *the eighth principle in discovering your true purpose in life. In partnership we learn and become empowered to discover our power-from-within in ourselves and power-with with others. We also learn to truly appreciate, value, and respect each other.* An old friend of mine likes to say, '*through partnership we learn to be as fully human as possible.*'"

"What?" said Mike.

"Let me put it this way," replied John. "Haven't you ever felt put down by someone who has power over you? And then bought into their criticism of you?"

"Of course, you are talking about pretty much every teacher or boss I ever had. And, yes, sometimes I believed them," said Mike, while watching Mary nod her head in agreement.

"Exactly," said John, "Well, in the hardware store we work as partners, meaning everyone has a stake in seeing the store and each other do well. We don't criticize each other, but we support each other to do our best. After all, if the hardware store does well, then we all do well."

"But aren't you the weekend manager? Meaning you are the boss?" asked Mary.

"Yes, I am, but all that means is that I'm responsible for opening and closing the store and coordinating the schedule of when which of my colleagues are coming in to work. And even this is something I try to accomplish after listening to everyone, and then I try to create a level of fairness. The important work, helping the customers, is everyone's responsibility. And the better we do that the more each of us earns because the weekend profit is split equally, creating a partnership-type atmosphere. This gives us all an incentive to want to do our best and support each other to do their best."

"Okay, sure this sounds good," said Mike, "I wish where I worked we had this partnership system, but how is this good for the planet?"

"Because, at least in this particular situation, we have created a system where we support each other to be the best we can be using power-with structures. And until the human race learns how to do this for everyone, then we are not going to solve our fundamental environmental problems," said John.

"I don't know, John, your ideas sound good, and I wish they could happen, but do you really think that people can stop telling others how to live and instead support them to find happiness or their true self?" asked Mary.

"Yes I do, Mary, under the idea that *we are all in this together*. I also truly believe we are not going to make it as a race unless we change," replied John.

"But John, what about Darwinism and survival of the fittest? I don't remember too much from high school biology, but I do remember that!" said Mike.

"I hear you, Mike, but there are two problems with Darwinism and survival of the fittest."

"Wait a second, what is Darwinism and survival of the fittest again?" asked Mary.

"Let's see if I can put Darwinism and his survival of the fittest theory in simple terms," said John. "Charles Darwin gave us the theory that others over time have interpreted as only the strongest of any species will survive in this dog-eat-dog world."

"Yeah, that sounds right," said Mike. "Only the strongest will survive, right?"

"Right. If we humans accept this interpretation of Darwinism as a fact of life (which is what we tend to do) and not just a mental model, then telling others how they should live their lives is fine because there are and always will be humans that are stronger and smarter than others, and consequently all the weak humans should listen to them," said John.

"That's pretty cruel, John!" said Mary. "My dad is a boss and I don't believe he thinks everyone below him is weaker or less smart than him."

"Of course not, but unconsciously most bosses do think their employees are not as smart as them, because our society taught them to think like that: 'Hey, I worked hard and I'm a boss now, so my experience makes me smarter.'"

"What you are saying is true, John, but what is wrong with that? I'm a boss because I do have ten years of experience at my place of work," said Mike.

"Mike, I don't doubt you worked hard and deserve to be a boss, but does that mean your bosses believe you are smarter than the people who work for you, and consequently expect you to tell them what they should do?" asked John.

"Well, yeah, I think they do, but this isn't a bad thing, John. I do know what my employees need to do, and they don't."

"Okay, and of course you explain to them what their job is and how you think they should do it initially, but once they have a handle on their job do you ever ask them how they can improve their job?"

"No, I cannot say I do," said Mike.

"Why not?" asked John.

"Truthfully, it never crossed my mind to. I figured someone above me figured out long ago the best way to do things and designed it that way," said Mike.

"And this is one of the things that is fundamentally wrong with society. We as a society or species think, granted mostly unconsciously, that Darwinism's theory of survival of the fittest is a fact. So unconsciously we buy into the 'fact' that there are people smarter or stronger than us that we have to listen to in order to survive."

"Again, what is wrong with that?" asked Mike.

"It stops us from trying to figure out who we are for ourselves!" exclaimed John.

After a moment of silence Mary said, "So, people are not inclined to try and discover their true self because they are not encouraged to?"

"Right, but it is worse than that. *Because our species buys into Darwinism as a law of nature, people are not only discouraged from trying to discover their true selves, others who think they know better feel it's their right to tell people how to think and live!*"

The group could see John felt passionate about what he was saying. "So, are you saying that Darwinism's survival of the fittest is not a fact or law of nature?" asked Mary.

"Correct, *Darwinism's survival of the fittest is NOT a fact or a law of nature, it is a mental model*," said John.

"Wow, John, are you saying there are no laws of nature?" asked Mary.

"No, there are laws of nature. The sun will definitely rise in the east every day, but Darwin's observations of nature are not laws."

"How do you know that?"

"Because other scientists have observed that for every example in nature that you can give me where we observe a survival of the fittest phenomenon, they can show you an example of where we will observe a symbiotic relationship phenomenon," said John.

"Symbiotic relationship?" said Mary.

"Partnership might be a better word," said John. "For example, biologists know that ants and bees cannot exist without each other. Together they form a partnership in order to survive. Unfortunately, Darwin did not observe this phenomenon, and consequently his followers became focused on the domination of one species over another and decided that was a universal law of nature. Today, we know that this isn't true, and yet society thinks and acts as if it is."

"And," said Mary, "this is not healthy for us because it leads us as a species to believe the only way to live is by dominating every other species, including our own. I get it! We not only are discouraged from trying to discover our true selves, but we are also encouraged to dominate each other and all other species." Mary paused for a moment and then continued, *"And this domination has led to us using up most of the world's resources with no thought of other species or even of our own future generations!"*

"Bingo!" replied John. "And, as I said a few minutes ago, until the human race learns how to create partnerships with each other and other living things, we are not going to solve our fundamental societal and environmental problems."

Chapter Twenty-Three

John got up to get himself another cup of coffee but realized he had had enough coffee and switched to cold water. Upon returning to the table he said, "All this talk about partnerships and everything being connected leads to the ninth principle to discovering your true purpose in life. *The ninth principle is that your true purpose is always part of something greater than yourself that makes the world a better place for more than just you.*"

When John finished making this statement Mary said, "Oh, I get it! Like being part of our cohousing."

"Exactly," said John. "Cohousing is an excellent example of being part of something greater than yourself. Can you think of others?"

Mike jumped in and said, "My high school baseball team!"

"Right!" replied John. "Teams are excellent examples being part of something that is greater than just yourself. Mike, how did it feel to be part of your high school baseball team?"

"It felt great! In fact, I don't think I have ever had a better feeling with other people, except for maybe my family," said Mike.

"I rest my case. Being part of a team or a family is being part of something greater than yourself," said John.

"And, as an entire unit, you are trying to make your life better for all of you!" Mary said. She paused and then added, "And, hopefully, for others."

"Well, all I can say is that when we were winning we made the whole town feel good. And even when we were losing the town was behind us," said Mike.

"But John, can't teams also be more than just sports teams?" asked Mary.

"Teams can be and are everywhere. I would say we are a team here in our cohousing," said John. "And teams can do boundless things. The great anthropologist Margaret Mead once said, *'Never doubt that a small group of thoughtful, committed citizens can change the world. Indeed, it's the only thing that ever has.'* I truly believe this, and we can see this everywhere around us."

"Or we can go back in history and see it too. How about our founding fathers? They created the Declaration of Independence, our Constitution, the Bill of Rights. These are incredible documents that we all try to live by," said Mike.

"We see it today with groups coming together to try to change to live healthier lives. Cohousing, local food cooperatives that bring us healthier foods, etc.," said Mary. "But this needs to happen in so many more ways if we are going to change the foundation of our whole society away from survival of the fittest and towards partnership and a focus on finding ways not to kill our planet."

"True, Mary, if you are an optimist like me then you believe we will build more partnerships. My feeling is we are in kindergarten as far as learning to live healthier and more sustainable lives. The principles I have outlined are not really new for the human race, but they are new for our society. The good news is these ideas are growing," said John.

Chapter Twenty-Four

"I agree with John. This conversation began with how the National Quality of Life indicator is up, meaning more people are living happy and meaningful lives. I can see how if someone discovers their true purpose and follows it they would feel their life was more meaningful, but what about happiness? Does a meaningful life automatically mean you are happy?" asked Mary.

"Yeah, I can think of several people who would say they have meaningful lives, but would also say they are happy when they are at the beach," said Dory who had just returned from the kitchen .

"Good question, Mary, and excellent observation, Dory. I think we are talking about two types of happiness: short-term, which is usually event-driven, and long-term, deeper, or real, happiness. The tenth principle for discovering your true purpose explains how a real, deeper happiness is integrated into someone's true purpose. *The tenth principle is that in discovering your true purpose in life it is important to understand that real, deeper happiness is a by-product of searching for, discovering, or accomplishing your true purpose in life.*"

"Okay, John, explain," said Mike.

"I learned through a wise friend, and trial and error, that happiness is not something you find in life by looking for it. When you hear someone say, 'I'm searching for happiness,' you can pretty much guarantee they are not going to find it. Oh, they might feel a fleeting moment of happiness when they do something that is fun like going to the beach, but this is usually followed by an emptiness that lasts much longer," said John.

"I remember in college we all looked forward to Friday and Saturday nights because we would party with our friends," said Dory.

"Oh yeah, I remember those days! I drank way too much beer in college, but it sure was fun," said Mike.

"Right, Mike, many of us drank too much, but even my friends that did not drink loved to dance, listen to whatever music, and hang out with their friends, and they looked forward to the weekend," said Dory. "My point is that partying in school was fun and made us happy, not because of the drinking but because we felt part of something bigger than ourselves. We had community. But later I watched many of these same people try and recreate our college parties in bars as adults, but in most bars there isn't community. Just a lot of drunk, stupid people trying to recreate community and failing."

"Dory, what are you trying to get at?" asked Mary.

"I'm agreeing with John. I watch people do things they say are going to make them happy – go out to a bar drinking, or shopping is a big one – but these are just events. And maybe for a moment these events make the person happy, but, I agree with John, this is followed by an emptiness that lasts much longer."

"So this is then followed by another event – shopping, going to the beach, drinking in a bar, etc. – they think is going to make them happy," John agreed. "And it might for a moment, but this again is followed by a longer feeling of emptiness, and the cycle goes on forever. Real, long-term happiness comes from searching for, discovering, or doing what you truly believe is why you were put on this earth."

"Okay, John, I think I understand what you mean by event," said Mike. "I've watched people my whole life say they can't wait for either Friday night, or golfing on Saturday, or the vacation they are going to take in a few weeks, or something else in the near future, and I always thought, 'what's wrong with right now that they can't wait for something in the future?'"

"Yeah, I have heard people say that they are happy, but all they do is complain about their lives, and I tend to think 'are they really happy?'" said Mary.

"No, they are not. At least not the deep, long-term happiness that comes with searching for and finding your true purpose in life," replied John.

John was silent for a minute to let the others think about what he had been saying. He then said, "Here is another similar principle. It pertains to materialism, which many people in our society believe brings them happiness. ***The eleventh principle to discovering your*** *true purpose in life is to know that it's better to have a few things and appreciate them, than a lot of things and not appreciate any of them."*

Mary said, "Duh," but then stopped to think for a moment and added, "Yes, I already know that, but I'll admit many people don't. In fact I learned a trick a long time ago to follow this principle." Mary pulled out her purse. "Every time I pull out my purse to buy something I ask myself, 'Do I really need this?' Many times the answer is no, so I don't buy it."

Mike then added, "As was already said earlier, knowing that materialism doesn't bring you happiness is growing, but what I like about what John said is that it's still okay to 'have things' as long as it's not a lot of things and the few things you do have you appreciate."

"I agree," said Sophie who had just walked in and joined the table. "When I realized material things were not only not bringing me happiness, but that pursuing more money so I could buy more things was actually stressing me out, I decided I needed to change my life. At first I thought I had to reject all material things and go live on a commune with a bunch of hippies, but then I realized I just needed to simplify my life and not give up everything. John, what was the eleventh principle again?"

"It's better to have a few things and appreciate them, than a lot of things and not appreciate any of them," said John.

"Yep, that's what I learned. You know one of the biggest de-stressors I figured out was when I realized I did not need to own a house to feel successful as a parent."

"Hey, that was my mental model too!" said Mary.

"What is a mental model?" asked Sophie.

"I promise I will tell you later," said Mary. "But first I want to go back to something I said earlier about when I realized that trying to own my own house was totally stressing me out. I grew up in a house owned by my family and we were not part of something greater. Hell, I didn't even know my neighbors, and my parents spent all their time in the city working in order for us to own this home," said Mary.

"Yeah, I grew up in a house like that. Bedroom communities are what they were called," said Sophie.

"But you are both correct that not owning your own home does not mean you are a bad parent," said Mike. "Besides, there is more real community in cohousing than there is in any suburban neighborhood."

Chapter Twenty-Five

The group was then silent for a while. It was clear they agreed with John and the eleventh principle, but they all realized they needed time to process what John had been saying. John, understanding this, said he needed to get back to his room and excused himself. Mary and the others said goodbye to John, and Mary began to explain to Sophie about mental models. Back in his room John said to Phred, "Phred, you would not believe the incredible conversation I just had with my friends."

"Cool, tell me about it, John?" asked Phred.

"Well it all started with someone talking about the National Quality of Life indicator and how we measure living happy and meaningful lives," said John. "This led to me explaining the principles of how to discover your true purpose in life. And you know, Phred, I think they got it!"

"Wow, John, it sounds like a great conversation," said Phred.

"It was," said John excitedly. "In many ways, I felt I was you! All those conversations we had over the years about mental models, everything being interconnected, etc. It was great Phred."

"It sounds like your time with your friends was more than just conversation. It sounds like it was more like dialogue. What's the twelfth principle of discovering your true purpose in life again?" asked Phred.

John knew Phred was just testing him so he said, "*The twelfth principle for discovering your true purpose in life is that, in order for power-with and power-from-within to flourish, dialogue must be the way we communicate with each other.*"

"That's it. So does that sound like what was happening with you and your friends today?" asked Phred.

"Yes, it does, Phred."

"That's great, John," said Phred. "Why don't we go watch the sunset and you can tell me more about the dialogue you had with your friends?"

The End

Epilogue:

Dear Reader:

As John said, and Phred would agree, the human race is in kindergarten in trying to save itself from itself. If we don't, the world will still be here but we won't be. Maybe the next species coming up the evolutionary ladder will do a better job than us, but unless we change *WE WILL NOT BE HERE*! Below are the twelve principles I have outlined to start the road I believe we need to go down. Will we? Well that really is up to you – the reader. Read them again. Begin the action-mindfulness observation-reflection-action process of discovering your true purpose in life. Learn to understand your mental models and start to change the unhealthy ones. Start a dialogue with your friends. Simplify your life. But before you do any of this, take a moment right now and just appreciate this moment, and then begin. Good luck
– Dan Gerber and Phred (July 2013)

THE PRINCIPLES:

Discovering your true purpose in life is a dance between trying new things, gaining a better understanding of who you are, and developing a deeper understanding of the world around you.

The second principle for discovering your true purpose in life is knowing there isn't any security in life, outside the security of knowing who you are, being that person to the best of your ability, and continuing growing and learning your entire life.

The third principle for discovering your true purpose in life is understanding your mental models and changing the unhealthy ones.

The fourth principle in discovering your true purpose is practicing mindfulness observation, being aware of the present moment. It slows down your thinking, helps you appreciate your life at that moment, and helps you observe your own thinking and discover your mental models.

The fifth principle for discovering your true purpose is that people learn 80% of what they discover for themselves, and learn best when what they are learning is useful to them.

The six principle of finding your true purpose in life is to understand that everything is interconnected, which includes the relationships you create with the world.

The seventh principle is that finding your true purpose is a life-long process and sometimes evolves or changes over time.

The eighth principle in discovering your true purpose in life is that in partnership we learn and become empowered to discover our power-from-within in ourselves and power-with with others. We also learn to truly appreciate, value, and respect each other.

The ninth principle is that your true purpose is always part of something greater than yourself that makes the world a better place for more than just you.

The tenth principle is that in discovering your true purpose in life it is important to understand that real, deeper happiness is a by-product of searching for, discovering, or accomplishing your true purpose in life.

The eleventh principle to discovering your true purpose in life is to know that it's better to have a few things and appreciate them, than a lot of things and not appreciate any of them.

The twelfth principle for discovering your true purpose in life is that in order for power-with and power-from-within to flourish and create partnership, dialogue must be the way we communicate with each other.